The
BIRD *of* BIOGRAPHIES
W.H. HUDSON

The BIRD *of* BIOGRAPHIES W.H. HUDSON

Author of Green Mansions

Foreword by JONATHAN MASLOW

CAPRA PRESS
SANTA BARBARA

Cover design by Maureen Lauran.
Illustrations by H. Gronvold.
Typesetting by Jim Cook.
Special acknowledgement to William Webb, Big Sur.

LIBRARY OF CONGRESS CATALOGING-IN-PUBLICATION DATA
Hudson, W.H. (William Henry), 1841–1922.
[Birds of La Plata. Selections]
The bird biographies of W.H. Hudson:
selected from "Birds of La Plata."
p. cm.
ISBN 0-88496-282-2 (pbk.) $8.95
1. Birds—Argentina. I. Title.
QL689.A6H81325 1988
598.2982—dc19   87-28567 CIP

CAPRA PRESS
Post Office Box 2068
Santa Barbara, California 93120

FOREWORD

Someone of his own generation once said that if W.H. Hudson could have molded the world to his liking it would have come out as one vast bird sanctuary: this only demonstrates how completely the man was misunderstood in his time.

Hudson was born on the pampas of Argentina in 1841, at about the same time that Thoreau was building his hut at Walden Pond—roughly contemporaneous with the forced removal of the Indians west of the Missisippi. He died in London in 1922, eight years after the lords of science and industry plunged the world into the fiery hell of the First World War. Hudson had known an immense, wild, and free part of the American hemisphere before Darwin published "Origin of the Species"; and he knew it not as some visiting European, self-consciously absorbing facts, but as a boy knows the neighborhood he grows up in: from the age of six Hudson was given a pony and allowed to ride out from his father's frontier *estancia*, a few miles from the Rio Plata, to wherever his spirit took him. He was a tall, strong boy, athletic and in perfect health, and from that early time he showed the *sine qua non* of the gifted naturalist—the stamina and curiosity to roam about alone outdoors. He was never dissuaded from being outdoors instead of studying.

The Argentine pampas at that time teemed with birds, snakes, and a large complement of unusual South American mammals (e.g., see Hudson's description of *vizcacha* "villages" in the bio of the Bank Martin, p. 20). A terrestrial sea of tall, waving, monochrome grasses stretched away from the gates of Buenos Aires for hundreds of miles, broken only by manmade atolls of trees planted round scattered ranchos, and by broad lagoons and marshes along the Rio Plata. Over these vast unfenced plains roamed an incredible multitude of half or wholly wild cattle, horses, sheep, and pigs, tended by the equally half or wholly wild *gauchos*. The hot wind of the interior, known as the *pampero*, would race across with cyclone force, and sudden hailstorms would literally knock herds over dead. Jaguars and pumas were among the top predators of the glades along the Rio Plata. And the lofty Rhea, or American ostrich, was a common sight, racing faster than anything with its odd habit of splaying one wing up "like a great sail." (bio. of Common Rhea, p. 201).

More than the grand diversity or sheer numbers of the animal and plant life on the pampas, the animistic gods had not as yet been tossed off the ranch. Hudson soon sensed their presence. Lying in bed listening to the night-migrating flocks of plovers, Hudson was inducted into that "enchanted realm, a nature at once natural and supernatural." ("Far Away and Long Ago," American edition, 1918). Then he would go out under the full moon and listen to the birds, the trees, the whispering grasses, experiencing something "similar to the feeling a person would have if visited by a supernatural being." (ibid) As his experiences in nature widened, he later felt the same sense of communion with reptiles—but never more so than with birds. In all the marvelous landscapes of South America that Hudson painted in his books are intimations of nature as earth spirit; but he was explicit in his belief that birds possess a soul, experience emotions, and appreciate beauty in their love songs and mating dances. In this he went beyond St. Francis—although Hudson never tried to preach to the birds.

There is a religion proper to desert nomads, and to fishermen on the shores, and to riders on the plains. Even Jesus of Nazareth says in the Gospel According to

Thomas, "The kingdom of the Father is spread upon the earth, and men do not see it." Animism, however, unlike the organized religions, takes its power from particular places. When nature is no longer the dominant presence there, her spell is broken. When one abandons that place, nature's power necessarily fades. Nonetheless, Hudson was never in his later life in England able to completely swallow the chilly Victorian dogma of natural selection. He remained something of a mystic, though a sane, skeptical, and reasonable one. It's true, but misses the point, that Hudson spent a good deal of time and energy in his old age writing blistering pamphlets against the slaughter of birds for ladies millinery, and for the liberation of all caged birds. The birds never had a better friend and champion than W.H. Hudson. But the nostalgia and sentimentality implied in the notion of a life dedicated to creating bird sanctuaries—sort of concentration camps for the losers after the war against nature is already over—would have outraged Hudson, who once described England as "a glorified poultry farm." It misses the central point of Hudson's spirited rebellion against our usurpation of nature, our wanton destruction of land and life, our doomed attempts to control the very processes of universal change. What Hudson wanted was not island refuges from industrial society, but to recreate the Argentine pampas of his boyhood, nothing less. And that's just what he used his writing to do.

The derivation of "Birds of La Plata," from which these life histories are drawn, is as follows. From about the age of 15, when sudden attacks of typhus and rheumatic fever nearly killed him, Hudson became a voracious reader. Through Gilbert White's "Natural History of Selbourne" he conceived the idea of making his native territory of La Plata his own "parish of

Selbourne." As he recovered his health, Hudson began keeping journals of his increasingly long field expeditions. Without time as a limiting factor, he patiently observed and recorded the most intimate habits of the birds—"Never was there a better describer of the habits of birds," wrote Wallace when he reviewed Hudson's book for *Nature.*

Besides developing the finest ear for bird-song, Hudson was also fascinated and moved by workings of adaptation and selection. His keen powers of observation led to numerous original discoveries, such as his note that the "Chimango," or Common Carrion Hawk, "removes its young when the nest has been discovered—a rare habit with birds." (bio. of Chimango, p. 106). His many references to birds' playfulness, and his joyous descriptions of their prenuptial dances, give a glimpse of the great things Hudson could have accomplished as an American naturalist had he remained in the land of his birth.

Instead, his expert knowledge led to introductions and offers from the Smithsonian Institution, and eventually from the London Zoological Society. He collected hundreds of "skins" for them, travelling as far as Patagonia, Brazil, and Uruguay—Hudson was a good shot and table hunter in his day, with an attitude toward killing more like the American Indian than the Victorian collector (later, a central tenet of his belief would be that sparing bird life was not just good for the individual animal but for the soul of man; he angrily withdrew from the British Ornithologists' Union when it refused to stop collectors from decimating threatened species).

By 1869 Hudson was publishing a series of letters on the birds and other animals of La Plata in the London Zoological Society's proceedings, which enticed him toward a literary career in England. In 1874, his journals bulging from decades of field notes as an intinerant naturalist, Hudson left Argentina forever to go to London. After fifteen years as a pathetic failure and obscure literary hack—reduced to marrying a boarding house landlady much older than himself—"Argentine Ornithology" was published in 1889; it was Hudson's first bird book. Even then his collaborator Philip Sclater of the London Zoological Society got top billing, although Hudson contributed all the raw material and firsthand accounts of the birds—everything, in fact, except the classification and synonymy.

There matters stood until 1920, two years before Hudson's death. The time of gilded optimism in the machine age was past. Instead of human progress and the bloom of civilization, the century ushered in total warfare and the severing of man's vital links to the natural world. The open and free pampas were "Far Away and Long Ago," as Hudson so aptly called his autobiographical memoir. But at last, fame and financial security were his. As Britain's grand old champion of bird conservation, Hudson decided to reissue his youthful ornithological field notes under the title "Birds of La Plata."

He cut all the Sclater material, claiming the book's original taxonomy had been "out of date as soon as published" because new species moved into the area and others left or were exterminated. The numerous references in "Birds of La Plata" to species cruelly and stupidly hunted to extinction lead one to believe Hudson added considerable material from his later perspective. He was probably correct by that time in his bittersweet estimate that the book's chief literary interest was that W.H. Hudson had written it. His new introduction, however, noted the ornithological reason for republication of "these little bird biographies": no other books on the same subject had been written in the intervening decades. Certainly, no better book on the ornithology of "the great bird continent," as Hudson liked to call South America, has ever come out since. To this day, Hudson's methodology in the field is the model for any wildlife biologist or serious birdwatcher. His strong, clarion voice is the envy of any writer of natural history.

Hudson lived long enough to deal with his own work in retrospect. He could see the prophetic value of his life histories. Along with "Far Away and Long Ago," they completed his journey back home. Life, the living bird, was the thing, he said, "not the dead stuffed specimen in the cabinet." For once the life goes out of bird or man "what is left is nothing but dust." Hudson felt "a pang" as he wrote these words over the grave of "that land so rich in bird life, those fresher woods and newer pastures, where I might have done so much." If man is to begin the Great Return to nature, on which his survival depends, he could find no better guide than W.H. Hudson, who loved life so profoundly.

—JONATHAN MASLOW

CONTENTS

(1920 nomenclature)

PATAGONIAN MOCKING-BIRD

Mimus patachonicus

Above and beneath grey, paler on the under surface and tinged with rufous on the belly; throat and eye-mark white; wings black; tail black, tipped with white; bill and feet black; eye olive-green; length 9.2 inches. Female smaller in size and lighter in colour.

THE Patagonian Mocking-bird, which I met with during my sojourn on the Rio Negro of Patagonia, closely resembles the species just described, but is smaller, the plumage is of a darker grey, and the irides are also of a darker green. It is a common bird, resident, lives alone or with its mate, feeds on insects and berries, and in its manner of flight and habits is like *Mimus modulator.* The nest is made in the centre of a bush of thorns and sticks, and lined with dry grass, cow-hair, or other soft material; the eggs are four in number, bluntly pointed, and thickly marked with dark flesh-coloured spots. When the nest is approached the parent birds come close to the intruder, often perching within a yard of his head, but without uttering any sound, differing in this respect from *M. modulator.*

The song of the Patagonian bird is in character like that of the northern species, the variety of its notes being apparently infinite; there are, however, some differences worth mentioning. The singing of the Patagonian species is perhaps inferior, his voice being less powerful, while his mellow and clear notes are constantly mingled with shrill ones, resembling the cries of some of the Dendrocolaptine birds. While incapable of notes so loud or so harsh as those of the northern bird, or of changes so wild and sudden, he possesses an even greater variety of soft notes. Day after day for many months I have heard them singing, yet never once listened to them for any length of time without hearing some note or phrase I had never heard before. The remarks I have made concerning the Calandria's mocking-faculties also apply to this bird : but though he does not actually repeat the notes and songs of other species, he certainly does mock the notes of individuals of his own species; for it must be borne in mind that no two individuals sing quite alike, and that the same bird constantly introduces new notes into his song, and never repeats his notes in the same order. I have often observed that when a bird while singing emits a few of these *new* notes, he seems surprised and delighted with them ; for, after a silent pause, he repeats them again and again a vast number of times, as if to impress them on his memory. When he once more resumes his varied singing, for hours and sometimes for days the expression he has discovered is still a favourite one, and recurs with the greatest frequency. But this is not all. If the new note or phrase happens to be a very striking one, it immediately takes the fancy of all the other birds within hearing, and often in a small thicket there will be a dozen or twenty birds near together, each sitting perched on the summit of his own bush. After the new wonderful note has been sounded they all become silent and attentive, reminding one in their manner of a caged Parrot listening to a sound it is trying to learn. Presently they learn it, and are as pleased with its acquisition as if they had dis-covered it themselves, repeating it incessantly. I noticed this curious habit of the bird many times, and on one occasion I found that for three entire days all the birds in a small thicket I used to visit every day did nothing but repeat incessantly two or three singular notes they had borrowed from one of their number. The constant repetition of this one sound had an irritating effect on me; but a day or two later they had apparently got tired of it themselves, and had resumed their usual varied singing.

This bird usually sits still upon the summit of a bush when singing, and its music is heard in all seasons and in all weathers from dawn till after dark : as a rule it sings in a leisurely, unexcited manner, remaining silent for some time after every five or six or a dozen notes, and apparently listening to his brother-performers. These snatches of melody often seem like a prelude or promise of something better coming; there is often in them such exquisite sweetness and so much variety that the hearer is ever wishing for a fuller measure, and still the bird opens his bill to delight and disappoint him, as if not yet ready to display his whole power.

WHITE-BANDED MOCKING-BIRD
Mimus triurus (Vieill.)

WHITE-BANDED MOCKING-BIRD

Mimus triurus

Above grey, brown on the rump; beneath light grey; wing black, crossed with a broad white band; tail white, except the two middle feathers which are black; bill and feet black; eye orange yellow; length 9.5 inches.

AZARA first met with this king of the Mocking-birds in Paraguay a century ago; he named it *Calandria de las tres colas,* and described the plumage accurately, but was, I think, mistaken about the colour of the eye, which is orange-red and not olive-green. He says that it is a rare species, possessing no melodious notes, which proves at once that he never heard it sing. D'Orbigny obtained it in Bolivia, Bridges in Mendoza, and more recently it has been found by collectors in various parts of the Argentine country, even in Buenos Ayres, where, however, it is probably only an occasional visitor. But they have told us nothing of its song and of its miraculous mocking-powers. For my part I can think of no other way to describe the surpassing excellence of its melody, which delights the soul beyond all other bird-music, than by saying that this bird is among song-birds like the diamond among stones, which in its many-coloured splendour represents and exceeds the special beauty of every other gem.

I met with this species on the Rio Negro in Patagonia; it was there called *Calandria blanca,* a name not strictly accurate, since the bird is not all white, but certainly better than Azara's strange invention of " Lark with three tails."

The bird was not common in Patagonia, and its only language was a very loud harsh startled note, resembling that of the *Mimus calandria;* but it was past the love-season when I first met with it, and

the natives all assured me that it possessed a very
wonderful song, surpassing the songs of all other
birds ; also that it had the faculty of imitating other
species. In manners and appearance it struck me as
being utterly unlike a *Mimus* ; in its flight and in
the conspicuous white and black of the wings and
tail it looked like a Tyrant of the *Tænioptera* group.
It was extremely shy, had a swift, easy, powerful
flight, and when approached would rise up high in
the air and soar away to a great distance. In February
it disappeared from the Rio Negro and did not
return till the following October, after the arrival of
all the other migrants. It was then that I had the
rare good fortune to hear it sing, and I shall never
forget the sensation I experienced when listening to
its matchless melody.

While walking through a *chañar*-wood one bright
morning, my attention was suddenly arrested by notes
issuing from a thicket close by, to which I listened in
delighted astonishment, so vastly superior in melody,
strength, and variety did they seem to all other bird-
music. That it was the song of a *Mimus* did not occur
to me ; for while the music came in a continuous
stream, until I marvelled that the throat of any bird
could sustain so powerful and varied a song for so
long a time, it was never once degraded by the harsh
cries, fantastical flights, and squealing buffooneries
so frequently introduced by the Calandria, but every
note was in harmony and uttered with a rapidity and
joyous abandon no other bird is capable of, except,
perhaps, the Skylark ; while the purity of the sounds
gave to the whole performance something of the
ethereal rapturous character of the Lark's song when
it comes to the listener from a great height in the air.

Presently this flow of exquisite unfamiliar music
ceased, while I still remained standing amongst the

trees, not daring to move for fear of scaring away the strange vocalist. After a short interval of silence I had a fresh surprise. From the very spot whence that torrent of melody had issued, burst out the shrill, confused, impetuous song of the small Yellow-and-Grey Patagonian Flycatcher (*Stigmatura flavo-cinerea*). It irritated me to hear this familiar and trivial song after the other, and I began to fear that my entertainer had flown away unobserved. But in another moment, from the same spot, came the mellow matin-song of the Diuca Finch, and this was quickly succeeded by the silvery bell-like trilling song of the Churrinche, or little Scarlet Tyrant-bird. Then followed many other familiar notes and songs —the flute-like evening call of the Crested Tinamu, the gay hurried twittering of the Black-headed Siskin, and the leisurely-uttered delicious strains of the Yellow Cardinal, all repeated with miraculous fidelity. How much was my wonder and admiration increased by the discovery that my one sweet singer had produced all these diverse strains! The discovery was only made when he began to repeat songs of species that never visit Patagonia. I knew then that I was at last listening to the famed White Mocking-bird, just returned from his winter travels, and repeating in this southern region the notes he had acquired in sub-tropical forests a thousand miles away.

These imitations at length ceased, after which the sweet vocalist resumed his own matchless song once more. I ventured then to creep a little nearer, and at length caught sight of him hardly fifteen yards away. I then found that the pleasure of listening to its melody was greatly enhanced when I could at the same time see the bird, so carried away with rapture does he appear while singing, so many and so beautiful are the gestures and motions with which his notes are accompanied. He passes incessantly from bush to bush, scarcely alighting on their summits, and at times dropping down beneath the foliage; then, at intervals, soaring to a height of a hundred feet above the thicket, with a flight slow as that of a Heron, or mounting suddenly upwards with a wild, hurried, zigzag motion; then slowly circling downwards, to sit with tail outspread and the broad glistening white wings expanded, or languidly waved up and down like the wings of some great butterfly —an object beautiful to see.

When I first heard this bird sing I felt convinced that no other feathered songster on the globe could compare with it; for besides the faculty of reproducing the songs of other species, which it possesses in common with the Virginian Mocking-bird, it has a song of its own, which I believed matchless; and in this belief I was confirmed when, shortly after hearing it, I visited England, and found of how much less account than this Patagonian bird, which no poet has ever praised, were the sweetest of the famed melodists of the Old World.

HOUSE-WREN

Troglodytes furvus

Warm brown; tail-feathers and outer webs of wing-feathers pen-
cilled with dark wavy lines; beneath pale brown; length 4.8 inches.

THE common Argentine Wren is to all English
residents the " House-Wren," and is considered to
be identical with the species familiar to them in
their own country. It is a sprightly little bird, of a
uniform brown colour and a cheerful melodious
voice; a tireless hunter after small spiders and
caterpillars in hedges, gardens, and outhouses, where
it explores every dark hole and cranny, hopping
briskly about with tail erect, and dropping frequent
little curtsies; always prompt to scold an intruder
with great emphasis; a great hater of cats.

It was my belief at one time that the Wren was
one of the little birds a cat could never catch; but
later on I discovered that this was a mistake. At my
home on the pampas we once had a large yellow tom-
cat exceedingly dexterous in catching small birds;
he did not, however, eat them himself, but used to
bring them into the house for the other cats. Two
or three times a day he would appear with a bird,
which he would drop at the door, then utter a loud
mew very well understood by the other cats, for they
would all fly to the spot in great haste, and the first
to arrive would get the bird. At one time I noticed
that he brought in a Wren almost every day, and,
curious to know how he managed to capture so
clever a bird, I watched him. His method was to go
out into the grounds frequented by Wrens, and seat
himself conspicuously amongst the weeds or bushes;

and then, after the first burst of alarm had subsided amongst the small birds, one or two Wrens would always take on themselves the task of dislodging him, or, at all events, of making his position a very uncomfortable one. The cat would sit perfectly motionless, apparently not noticing them at all, and by-and-by this stolid demeanour would have its effect, and one of the Wrens, growing bolder, would extend his dashing little incursions to within a few inches of pussy's demure face ; then at last, swift as lightning, would come the stroke of a paw, and the little brown body would drop down with the merry, brave little spirit gone from it.

The House-Wren is widely distributed in South America, from the tropical forests to the cold uplands of Patagonia, and, possessing a greater adaptiveness than most species, it inhabits every kind of country, moist or dry, and is as much at home on lofty mountains and stony places as in the everglades of the Plata, where it frequents the reed-beds and damp forests. About houses they are always to be found ; and though the traveller on the desert pampas might easily imagine that there are no Wrens in the giant grasses, if he makes himself a lodge in this lonely region, a Wren will immediately appear to make its nest in his thatch and cheer him with its song.

Even in large towns they are common, and I always remember one flying into a church in Buenos Ayres one Sunday, and during the whole sermon-time pouring out its bright lyric strain from its perch high up somewhere in the ornamental woodwork of the roof.

The Wren sings all summer, and also on bright days in winter. The song is not unlike that of the European Wren, having the same gushing character, the notes strong and clear, uttered with rapidity and

precision ; but the Argentine bird has greater sweetness and power ; although I cannot agree with Azara
that it resembles or comes nearest to the Nightingale.

In spring the male courts his mate with notes high
and piercing as the squeals of a young mouse ; these
he repeats with great rapidity, fluttering his wings
all the time like a moth, and at intervals breaking out
into song.

The nest is made in a hole in a wall or tree,
sometimes in the forsaken domed nest of some other
bird ; and where such sites are not to be found,
in a dense thistle or thorn-bush, or in a large tussock
of grass. I have also found nests in dry skulls of
cows and horses, in an old boot, in the sleeve of an
old coat left hanging on a fence, in a large-necked
bottle, and in various other curious situations. The
nest is built of sticks and lined with horsehair or
feathers, and the eggs are usually nine in number, of a
pinkish ground-colour, thickly spotted with pale red.

BANK-MARTIN

Atticora cyanoleuca

Above dark glossy blue; quills and tail-feathers black; cheeks and under surface pure white; sides of the neck blue, descending in a half-crescent on the sides of the chest; length 4.7 inches.

THIS diminutive dark-plumaged species is the smallest of our Hirundines. In Buenos Ayres they appear early in September, arriving before the Martins, but preceded by the Common Swallow. They are bank-birds, breeding in forsaken holes and burrows, for they never bore into the earth themselves, and are consequently not much seen about the habitations of man. They sometimes find their breeding-holes in the banks of streams, or, in cultivated districts, in the sides of ditches, and even down in wells. But if in such sites alone fit receptacles for their eggs were met with, the species, instead of one of the commonest, would be rare indeed with us; for on the level pampas most of the water-courses have marshy borders, or at most but low and gently sloping banks. But the burrowing habits of two other animals—the Vizcacha (*Lagostomus trichodactylus*), the common large rodent of the pampas, and the curious little bird called Minera (*Geositta cunicularia*)—have everywhere afforded the Martins abundance of breeding-places on the plains, even where there are no streams or other irregularities in the smooth surface of the earth.

The Minera bores its hole in the sides of the Vizcacha's great burrow, and in this burrow within a burrow the Martin lays its eggs and rears its young, and is the guest of the Vizcacha and as much dependent on it as the House-Wren and the Domestic

Swallow on man; so that in spring, when this species returns to the plains, it is in the villages of the Vizcachas that we see them. There they live and spend the day, sporting about the burrows, just as the Common Swallow does about our houses; and to a stranger on the pampas one of these villages, with its incongruous bird and mammalian inhabitants, must seem a very curious sight in the evening. Before sunset the old male Vizcachas come forth to sit gravely at the mouths of their great burrows. One or two couples of Mineras, their little brown bird-tenants, are always seen running about on the bare ground round the holes, resting at intervals with their tails slowly moving up and down, and occasionally trilling out their shrill laughter-like cry. Often a pair of Burrowing-Owls also live in the village, occupying one of the lesser disused burrows; and round them all flit half a dozen little Martins, like twilight moths with long black wings. It is never quite a happy family, however, for the Owls always hiss and snap at the Vizcacha if he comes too near; while the little Martins never become reconciled to the Owls, but perpetually flutter about them, protesting against their presence with long complaining notes.

The nest, made of dry grass lined with feathers, is placed at the extremity of the long, straight, cylindrical burrow, and contains five or six white pointed eggs. I have never seen these Martins fighting with the Minera to obtain possession of the burrows, for this industrious little bird makes itself a fresh one every spring, so that there are always houses enough for the Martins. After the young have flown, they sit huddled together on a weed or thistle-top, and the parents continue to feed them for many days.

As in size and brightness of plumage, so in language is the Bank-Martin inferior to other species, its only song being a single weak trilling note, much prolonged, which the bird repeats with great frequency when on the wing. Its voice has ever a mournful, monotonous sound, and even when it is greatly excited and alarmed, as at the approach of a fox or hawk, its notes are neither loud nor shrill. When flying they glide along close to the earth, and frequently alight on the ground to rest, which is contrary to the custom of other Swallows. Like other species of this family, they possess the habit of gliding to and fro before a traveller's horse, to catch the small twilight-moths driven up from the grass. A person riding on the pampas usually has a number of Swallows flying round him, and I have often thought that more than a hundred were before my horse at one time ; but from the rapidity of their motions it is impossible to count them. I have frequently noticed individuals of the four most common species following me together ; but after sunset, and when the other species have long forsaken the open grassy plain for the shelter of trees and houses, the diminutive Bank-Martin continues to keep the traveller company. At such a time, as they glide about in the dusk of evening, conversing together in low tremulous tones, they have a peculiarly sorrowful appearance, seeming like homeless little wanderers over the great level plains.

When the season of migration approaches they begin to congregate in parties not very large, though sometimes as many as one or two hundred individuals are seen together ; these companies spend much of their time perched close together on weeds, low trees, fences, or other slightly elevated situations, and pay little heed to a person approaching, but seem preoccupied or preyed upon by some trouble that has no visible cause.

The time immediately preceding the departure of the Martins is indeed a season of very deep interest to the observer of nature. The birds in many cases seem to forget the attachment of the sexes and their songs and aerial recreations; they already begin to feel the premonitions of that marvellous instinct that urges them hence: not yet an irresistible impulse, it is a vague sense of disquiet; but its influence is manifest in their language and gestures, their wild manner of flight, and their listless intervals.

The little Bank-Martin disappears immediately after the Purple Martins. Many stragglers continue to be seen after the departure of the main body; but before the middle of March not one remains, the migration of this species being very regular.

LONG-TAILED REED-FINCH

Donacospiza albifrons

Above yellowish grey, the back striped with blackish; lesser wing-coverts clear grey; greater coverts and quills black; head like back, greyish in the cheeks; eye-stripe and under surface buff; length 6 inches.

THE slender body, great length of tail, and the hue of the plumage, assimilating to that of sere decaying vegetation, might easily lead one into mistaking this Finch for a *Synallaxis* where these birds are abundant.

I have met with it in the marshy woods and reed-beds along the shores of the Plata, but it is a shy, rare bird in Buenos Ayres. I have followed it about, hoping to hear it utter a song or melodious note, but it had only a little chirp. I would not, however, on this account pronounce it to be the one silent member of a voiceful family, as my acquaintance with it is so very slight.

RED-BILLED GROUND-FINCH

Embernagra platensis

Above dull olive-green, striped with blackish; wings silky olive-green, the inner webs of the feathers black; edge of wings yellow; tail-feathers dull olive-green; beneath grey, belly buff; beak bright red; length 8.8 inches.

In this Finch the plumage is alike in both sexes. Above it is dusky olive-green, beneath grey; the beak is of a fine bright red. In Argentina this bird is most common in the littoral forests along the Plata, but ranges as far south as the Rio Negro in Patagonia. It does not migrate, nor associate in flocks; but the sexes are faithful, and the male and female are invariably together, and appear to be very fond of each other's society. They have a loud, sharp alarm chirp or cry, which bursts from the bird with the startling suddenness of a sneeze from a human being; also a confused unmelodious song, which always reminds me, in its hurry, vehemence, and peculiar sound, of the gobbling of a turkey-cock. They are not shy, but when approached sit jerking their tails about, and uttering loud chirps as if greatly excited. The flight is very curious; the bird springs up with great suddenness, and with tail erect, the long legs dangling down like a Rail's, and proceeds by a series of irregular jerks, violently shutting and opening its wings. They breed on the ground under the grass, and conceal their nest so well that I doubt whether the parasitical *Molothrus* ever finds it. I have at all events never seen them followed by the young of *Molothrus* demanding food.

As a rule small seed-eating birds are beneficially affected by the presence of man; thus our common

Zonotrichia and other sparrows and finches have
become excessively numerous in the most thickly-
settled districts. With the Red-billed Finch, however,
just the contrary has happened; and since I have
known this species it has disappeared from many
localities where it was once quite common. Azara's
name for this species, *Habia de bañado*, signifies that
it is a marsh bird; but though now found chiefly
in marshy situations, it was once common enough
over the entire pampas region, before the great
plains were settled on by Europeans. The bird is
very badly protected by nature against raptorial
species, owing to its very conspicuous red beak, its
habit of perching on the summit of tall plants and
other elevated positions, its loud impetuous voice,
which invites attention, and the weak eccentric
flight, which challenges pursuit. It is essential to
its safety that it should have, in the open country
it frequents, a dense grass cover into which it can
plunge on the slightest alarm. Where cattle are
introduced, the original pampas-grass which afforded
the suitable conditions disappears, giving place to
the soft, perishable grasses, clovers, and thistles of
Europe. Where these changes take place, the bird
cannot escape from its enemies and quickly disappears; while many Dendrocolaptine species inhabiting the same situations are saved by their
inconspicuous protective colouring, sharp wedge-like
bodies, and swift mouse-like motions on the ground.
In marshy places on the pampas, abounding with
long aquatic grasses and reed-beds, the Red-bill
still maintains its existence, but from its old habitat
on the open grassy plains, where it was once the
dominant Finch, it has utterly vanished.

YELLOW HOUSE-SPARROW

Sycalis pelzelni

Above yellowish olive-green, the back sparsely striped with blackish ;
wing- and tail-feathers black, edged with yellow ; forehead bright
orange, the rest of the head like the back ; below bright yellow ;
under surfaces of wings and tail also yellow ; length 5.4 inches.
Female dull brownish grey mottled with blackish above ; under surface whitish grey, striped with dusky brown on the breast ; wing-
and tail-feathers edged with yellow.

THE Yellow " House-Sparrow," as this species is
called, is the town-bird of Buenos Ayres, but does
not multiply greatly, nor is he familiar with man,
like his rough, sooty-plumaged, far-away London
relation.[1]

The forehead of the male is bright orange, the
prevailing colour of the entire plumage yellow,
clouded with other hues. The female is grey, marked
with pale fuscous, and is less in size than her mate.
They remain with us all the year and live in pairs,
the sexes in this species being faithful. Sometimes
they are seen associating in small flocks, but I am
inclined to believe that only the young unmated
birds are gregarious. In 1867-8, during the cholera
epidemic in Buenos Ayres, the Sparrows all disappeared from the town, and I was told by the
manager of a large steam flour-mill in the town that
the birds had not gone away, but had died. They
were found dead all about the mill, where they had
been very abundant. My informant was a careful
observer, and I have no doubt that he was correct
in what he told me.

[1] Alas! since this was first written in 1888 the "far-away" relation has
invaded Buenos Ayres, and as in so many other countries has become a pest.
One result of its appearance has been the vanishing of the pretty and
engaging Yellow House-Sparrow.

In spring and summer the male sings frequently
with great energy, but without much melody. After
a hurried prelude of sharp chirps and trills, he pours
out a continuous stream of sound, composed of
innumerable brief notes, high and shrill as those of
a bat, wounding the ear with their excessive sharp-
ness, and emitted so rapidly that the whole song is
more like that of a cicada than of a bird. This piercing
torrent of sound is broken at intervals by a long,
grave note, or half a dozen short, rapid notes in a
lower key, which come as an agreeable relief.

In towns they build in walls, like the English
Sparrow ; in country places they always select the
domed nest of some Dendrocolaptine species to
breed in. Possibly in some districts where I have
not been, this Sparrow selects other breeding-sites ;
my experience is that outside of a town it never lays
anywhere but in some domed nest, and at home I
frequently put up boxes for them in the trees, but
they would not notice them, though the Wrens and
Swallows were glad to have them. Sometimes they
make choice of the large fabric of the *Anumbius
acuticaudatus,* called Leñatero in the vernacular ;
but their claim to this nest (even when the Leñateros
are out of it) is frequently disputed by other species
which possess the same habit as this Sparrow, but
are more powerful than he. Their favourite breeding-
place is, however, the solid earthen structure of the
Oven-bird ; and it is wonderful to see how persistently and systematically they labour to drive out
the lawful owners—birds so much larger and more
powerful than themselves. Early in spring, and
before the advent of the Tree-Martins, the pair of
Sparrows begin haunting the neighbourhood of the
oven they have elected to take possession of, usually
one pretty high up in a tree. As the season advances

their desire towards it increases, and they take up their position on the very tree it is in ; and finally a particular branch near the oven, commanding a good view of the entrance, is chosen for a permanent resting-place. Here they spend a great portion of their time in song, twitterings, and loving dalliance, and, if attentively observed, they are seen with eyes ever fixed on the coveted abode. As the need for a receptacle for the eggs becomes more urgent they grow bolder, and in the absence of the owners flit about the oven, alight on it, and even enter it. The Oven-bird appears to drive them off with screams of indignation, but the moment he retires they are about it again, and, even when it contains eggs or young birds, begin impudently carrying in feathers, straws, and other materials for a nest, as if they were already in undisputed possession. At this stage the Tree-Martins (*Progne tapera*) perhaps appear to complicate matters ; and even if these last comers do not succeed in ousting the Oven-birds, they are sure to seize the oven when it becomes vacant, and the Sparrows, in spite of their earlier claim, are left out in the cold. But they do not take their defeat quietly, or, rather, they do not know when they are beaten, but still remain to harass their fellow pirates, just as they did the Oven-birds before, bringing straws and feathers in their beaks, and when forced to drop these materials and chased from the neighbourhood with great noise and fury by the Tree-Martins, it is only to return undaunted in a few minutes, bringing more straws and feathers.

This Sparrow makes a rather large nest, neatly lined with horsehair, and lays five eggs, long, pointed, the entire surface thickly matted with deep chocolate brown.

In rural districts this species is comparatively

rare, not more than one or two couples being seen about each habitation ; and I scarcely think it would be too much to say that there are four or five thousand Chingolos for every individual Yellow Sparrow. Yet it is a hardy little bird, well able to hold its own, subsists on the same kind of food and lays as many eggs as the *Zonotrichia* ; and it possesses, moreover, a great advantage over the dominant species in placing its nest out of the reach of the parasitical *Molothrus*, the destroyer of about fifty per cent. of the Chingolo's eggs. I can only attribute the great disparity in the numbers of the two species to the fact that the Yellow House-Sparrow will breed only (out of towns) in nests not easily taken, and to the stubborn pertinacity which leads it to waste the season in these vain efforts, while the other species is rearing its brood. This is a blunder of instinct comparable to that of the Minera (*Geositta cunicularia*), mentioned by Darwin in the *Voyage of a Naturalist*, where the bird made its hole in a mud wall a few inches wide, and on coming out on the other side simply went back and made another hole, and then another, unable to understand that the wall had not the requisite thickness.

In such a case as the Yellow House-Sparrow presents, in which the colour of the sexes differs, the female being without any of the brighter hues found in the male, and which makes an elaborate nest and lays deeply-coloured eggs, it is impossible not to believe that the bird originally built in exposed situations, and subsequently—perhaps in very recent times—acquired the habit of breeding in dark holes. The frequent destruction of the exposed nest, and an abundance of vacant domed nests, into which some individuals occasionally penetrated to breed, would lead to the acquisition of such a nesting-habit; for the birds inheriting it would have an advantage and be preserved, while those persisting in the old habit of building exposed nests would perish. Domed nests made by Dendrocolaptine birds are very abundant even now, and it is probable that, before the country became settled by Europeans, they were very much more numerous. Darwin, speaking of the Oven-bird's habit of always placing its oven in the most conspicuous and (to man) accessible places, predicts, and truly I believe, that this habit will eventually cause the extinction of the species; for when the country becomes more thickly settled, the bird-nesting boys will destroy all the ovens. Probably when the Oven-birds were more abundant the Sparrows could always find vacant ovens to breed in, until a habit of breeding almost exclusively in these safe and convenient bird-built houses was acquired; and the present seemingly stupid persistence of the birds in struggling to get possession of those already occupied by stronger species, only shows that the habit or instinct has not been modified to suit a change in the conditions— *i.e.*, a diminishing number of ovens to breed in, with perhaps the increase of other stronger species possessing the same habit. But while the instinct thus survives too strongly in the country birds, many individuals have taken to a town life, and acquired the new habit of breeding in holes in brick walls. Probably this race of town birds will eventually colonise the rural districts, and usurp the place of the country birds, which will then be placed at a disadvantage.

Upper—BAY-WINGED COW-BIRD
Molothrus badius (Vieill.)

Lower—SCREAMING COW-BIRD
Molothrus rufoaxillaris, Cassin.

SCREAMING COW-BIRD

Molothrus rufoaxillaris

Silky black glossed with purple; wings and tail with a slight greenish gloss; bill and feet black; length 8 inches. Female the same; slightly smaller.

THIS bird has no vulgar name, not being distinguished from the Common Cow-bird by the country people. The English name of Screaming Cow-bird, which I have bestowed on it, will I think commend itself as appropriate to those who observe it, for they will always and at any distance be able to distinguish it from the species it resembles so nearly by listening to its impetuous screaming notes, so unlike anything in the language of the Common Cow-bird.

The Screaming Cow-bird is larger than the allied species. The female is less than the male in size, but in colour they are alike, the entire plumage being deep blue-black, glossy, with purple reflections, and under the wing at the joint there is a small rufous spot. The beak is very stout, the plumage loose, with a strong musky smell; the œsophagus remarkably wide.

It is far less common than the other species of *Molothrus*, but not rare, and ranges south to the Buenos-Ayrean pampas, where a few individuals are usually found in every large plantation; and, like the Bay-winged Cow-bird, it remains with us the whole year. It is not strictly gregarious, but in winter goes in parties, seldom exceeding half a dozen individuals, and in the breeding-season in pairs. One of its most noteworthy traits is an exaggerated hurry and bustle thrown into all its movements. When passing from one branch to another, it goes by a

series of violent jerks, smiting its wings loudly
together; and when a party of them return from
the fields they rush wildly and loudly screaming to
the trees, as if pursued by a bird of prey. They are
not singing-birds; but the male sometimes, though
rarely, attempts a song, and utters, with considerable
effort, a series of chattering unmelodious notes.
The chirp with which he invites his mate to fly has
the sound of a loud and smartly given kiss. His
warning or alarm note when approached in the
breeding-season has a soft and pleasing sound; it
is, curiously enough, his only mellow expression.
But his most common and remarkable vocal performance is a cry beginning with a hollow-sounding
internal note, and swelling into a sharp metallic
ring; this is uttered with tail and wings spread and
depressed, the whole plumage raised like that of a
strutting turkey-cock, whilst the bird hops briskly
up and down on its perch as if dancing. From its
puffed-out appearance, and from the peculiar character of the sound it emits, I believe that, like the
Pigeon and some other species, it has the faculty of
filling its crop with air, to use it as a " chamber of
resonance." The note I have described is quickly
and invariably followed by a scream, harsh and
impetuous, uttered by the female, though both
notes always sound as if proceeding from one bird.
When on the wing the birds all scream together in
concert.

The food of this species is chiefly minute seeds
and tender buds; they also swallow large caterpillars and spiders, but do not, like their congeners,
eat hard insects.

I became familiar, even as a small boy, with the
habits of the Screaming Cow-bird, and before this
species was known to naturalists, but could never

find its nest though I sought diligently for it. I could never see the birds collecting materials for a nest, or feeding their grown-up young like other species, and this might have made me suspect that they did not hatch their own eggs; but it never occurred to me that the bird was parasitical, I suppose because in summer they are always seen in pairs, the male and female being inseparable. Probably this is the only parasitical species in which there is conjugal fidelity. I also noticed that when approached in the breeding-season the pair always displayed great excitement and anxiety, like birds that have a nest, or that have selected a site on which to build one. But year after year the end of the summer would arrive, the birds re-unite in parties of half a dozen, and the mystery remain unsolved. At length, after many years, fortune favoured me, and while observing the habits of another species (*Molothrus badius*) I discovered by chance the procreant habits of the Screaming Cow-birds; and as these observations throw some light on the habits of *M. badius* I think it best to transcribe my notes here in full.

A pair of Leñateros (*Anumbius acuticaudatus*), or Firewood-Gatherers, have been nearly all the winter building a nest on an acacia tree sixty yards from the house; it is about 27 inches deep, and 16 or 18 in circumference, and appears now nearly finished. I am sure that this nest will be attacked before long, and I have resolved to watch it closely.

September 28.—To-day I saw a Bay-wing (*M. badius*) on the nest; it climbed over it, deliberately inspecting every part with the critical air of a proprietor who had ordered its construction, taking up and re-arranging some sticks and throwing others away from the nest. While thus engaged, two

Common Cow-birds (*M. bonariensis*), male and female, came to the tree; the female dropped on to the nest, and began also to examine it, peering curiously into the entrance and quarrelling with the first bird. After a few minutes she flew away, followed by her glossy consort. The Bay-wing continued its strange futile work until the owners of the nest appeared, whereupon it hopped aside in its usual slow leisurely manner, sang for a few moments, then flew away. The similarity in the behaviour of the two birds struck me very forcibly; in the great interest they take in the nests of other birds, especially large covered nests, the two species are identical. But when the breeding-season comes their habits begin to diverge; then the Common Cow-bird lays in nests of other species, abandoning its eggs to their care; while the Bay-wings usually seize on the nests of other birds and rear their own young. Yet, as they do occasionally build a neat elaborate nest for themselves, the habit of taking possession of the nests of other birds is most likely a recently acquired one, and probably its tendency is to eradicate the original building instinct.

October 8.—This morning, while reading under a tree, my attention was aroused by a shrill note, as of a bird in distress, issuing from the neighbourhood of the Firewood-Gatherer's nest; after hearing it repeated at intervals for over twenty minutes, I went to ascertain the cause. Two Bay-wings flew up from the ground under the nest, and on searching in the rank clover growing under the tree, I discovered the female Leñatero, with plumage wet and draggled, trembling and appearing half dead with the rough treatment she had experienced. I put her in the sun, and after half an hour, hearing her mate calling, she managed to flutter feebly away to join him. The persecutors had dragged her out of the nest, and would, no doubt, have killed her had I not come so opportunely to the rescue.

Since writing the above I have continued to watch the nest. Both the Bay-wings and their victims left it for some days. Six days after I had picked up the ill-treated female, the builders of the nest came back and resumed possession. Four days later the Bay-wings also came back; but on finding the nest still occupied they took possession of an unfinished oven of an Oven-bird on another tree within twenty yards of the first, and immediately began carrying in materials with which to line it. When they had finished laying I took their five eggs, at the same time throwing down the oven, and waited to see what their next move would be. They remained on the spot, singing incessantly, and still manifesting anxiety when approached. I observed them four days, and then was absent from home as many more; on returning I found that the Leñateros had once more disappeared, and that the nest was now held by the Bay-wings. I also noticed that they had opened an entrance very low down at the side of the nest which they were using; no doubt they had killed and thrown out the young birds.

It was now early in November, the height of the breeding-season, and numbers of Common Cow-birds constantly visited the nest; but I was particularly interested in a pair of Screaming Cow-birds that had also begun to grow fond of it, and I resolved to watch them closely. As they spent so much of their time near the nest, showing great solicitude when I approached it, I strongly hoped to see them breed in it, if the Bay-wings could only be got rid of. The Screaming Cow-birds would not, or dare not, attack them. I therefore resolved to take the Bay-wings' eggs, hoping that that would cause them to leave in disgust.

When I was satisfied from their movements that they had finished laying, I got up to the nest, and was astonished to find *ten* eggs instead of five as I had confidently expected; for though the Common Cow-birds had paid a great deal of attention to the nest, I knew the Bay-wings would not allow *them* to lay in it.

The ten eggs in the nest were all unmistakably Bay-wings' eggs; and having observed before that several females do occasionally lay together, I concluded that in this case two females had laid in the nest, though I had only seen two birds—male and female. After taking the ten eggs the Bay-wings still remained, and in a very short time they appeared to be laying again. When I had reason to think that the full complement was laid, I visited the nest and found five eggs in it; these I also took, and concluded that the second female had probably gone away, after having been deprived of her first clutch. During all this time the Screaming Cow-birds remained in the neighbourhood and occasionally visited the tree; but to my very great surprise the Bay-wings still stubbornly remained, and by-and-by I found that they were going to lay again—the fourth time! When I next visited the nest there were two eggs in it; I left them and returned three days later, expecting to find five eggs, but found seven! certainly more than one female had laid in the nest on this occasion. After I had taken these last seven eggs the Bay-wings left; and though the Screaming Cow-birds continued to make occasional visits to the nest, to my great disappointment they did not lay in it.

April 12.—To-day I have made a discovery, and

am as pleased as if I had found a new planet in the sky. The mystery of the Bay-wings' nest twice found containing over the usual complement of eggs is cleared up, and I have now suddenly become acquainted with the procreant instinct of the Screaming Cow-bird. I look on this as a great piece of good fortune; for I had thought that the season for making any such discovery was already over, as we are so near to winter.

The Bay-wings are so social in their habits that they always appear reluctant to break up their companies in the breeding-season; no sooner is this over, and while the young birds are still fed by the parents, all the families about a plantation unite into one flock. About a month ago all the birds about my home had associated in this way together, and went in a scattered flock, frequenting one favourite feeding-spot very much, a meadow about fifteen minutes' walk from the house. The flock was composed, I believe, of three families, sixteen or eighteen birds in all : the young birds are indistinguishable from the adults ; but I knew that most of these birds were young, hatched late in the season, from their incessant strident hunger notes. I first observed them about the middle of March. A week ago, while riding past the meadow where they were feeding, I noticed among them three individuals with purple spots on their plumage. They were at a distance from me, and I naturally concluded that they were young Common Cow-birds (*M. bonariensis*), casually associating with the Bay-wings. I was surprised to see them, for the young male *M. bonariensis* always acquires the purple plumage before March, so that these individuals were changing colour five weeks after the usual time.

To-day, while out with my gun, I came upon the

flock, and noticed four of the birds assuming the
purple plumage, two of them being almost entirely
that colour ; but I also noticed with astonishment
that they had bay- or chestnut-coloured wings, also
that those with least purple on them were marvellously like the Bay-wings in the mouse-coloured
plumage of the body and the dark tail. I had seen
these birds before the purple plumage was acquired,
and there was then not the slightest difference amongst
them, the adults and their supposed offspring being
alike ; now some of them appeared to be under-
going the process of a transmutation into another
species ! I at once shot the four spotted birds, along
with two genuine Bay-wings, and was delighted to
find that the first were young Screaming Cow-birds.

I must now believe that the extra eggs twice
found in the nest of the Bay-wings were those of
the Screaming Cow-bird, that the latter species
lays chiefly in the nests of the former, that
the eggs of the two species are identical in form,
size, and colour, each bird also laying five, and
that, stranger still, the similarity is as perfect in
the young birds as it is in the eggs.

April 15.—This morning I started in quest of
the Bay-wings, and observed one individual, that
had somehow escaped detection the day before,
assuming the purple dress. This bird I shot ; and
after the flock had re-settled a short distance off, I
crept close up to them, under the shelter of a hedge,
to observe them more narrowly. One of the adults
was closely attended by three young birds ; and
these all, while I watched them, fluttered their wings
and clamoured for food every time the old bird
stirred on its perch. The three young birds seemed
precisely alike ; but presently I noticed that one of
them had a few minute purple spots, and on shooting

this one I found it to be a young *M. rufoaxillaris*, while the other two were true young Bay-wings.

The hunger-cry of the young *M. badius* (Bay-wing) is quite different from that of the young *M. bonariensis* : the cry of the latter is a long, shrill, two-syllabled note, the last syllable being prolonged into a continuous squeal when the foster-parent approaches with food ; the cry of the young *M. badius* is short, reedy, tremulous, and uninflected. The resemblance of the young *M. rufoaxillaris* to its foster-brothers in language and plumage is the more remarkable when we reflect that the adult bird in its habits, gestures, guttural notes, also in its deep purple plumage, comes much nearer to *M. bonariensis* than to *M. badius*. It seems impossible for mimicry to go further than this. A slight difference in size is quite imperceptible when the birds are flying about ; while in language and plumage the keenest ornithologist would not be able to detect a difference. It may, however, be questioned whether this is really a case of an external resemblance of one species to another acquired by natural selection for its better preservation. Possibly the young *M. rufoaxillaris*, in the first stage of its plumage, exhibits the ancestral type—that of the progenitor of both species. If *M. badius* belonged to some other group—*Sturnella* or *Pseudoleistes* for instance—it would scarcely be possible to doubt that the resemblance of the young *M. rufoaxillaris* to its foster-brothers resulted from mimicry ; but as both species belong to the limited well-defined group *Molothrus*, the resemblance may be ascribed to community of descent.

Formerly I believed that though *M. badius* is constantly seen rearing its own young, they also occasionally dropped their eggs in the nests of other birds. I could not doubt that this was the case after

having witnessed a couple of their young following
a Yellow-breast, *Pseudoleistes virescens*, and being fed
by it. I must now alter my opinion, for what then
appeared to be proof positive is now no proof at all,
for those two birds were probably the young of *M.
rufoaxillaris*. There are, however, good reasons for
believing that *M. rufoaxillaris* is parasitical almost
exclusively on *M. badius*. I have spoken of the many
varieties of eggs *M. bonariensis* lays. Those of *M.
badius* are a trifle less in size, in form elliptical, densely
and uniformly marked with small spots and blotches
of dark reddish colour, varying to dusky brown ; the
ground - colour is white, but sometimes, though
rarely, pale blue. It is not possible to confound the
eggs of the two species. Now ever since I saw, many
years ago, the Yellow-breast feeding the supposed
young Bay-wings, I have looked out for the eggs of
the latter in other birds' nests. I have found hundreds
of nests containing eggs of *M. bonariensis*, but never
one with an egg of *M. badius*, and, I may now add,
never one with an egg of *M. rufoaxillaris*. It
is wonderful that *M. rufoaxillaris* should lay only
in the nests of *M. badius* ; but the most mysterious
thing is that *M. bonariensis*, indiscriminately parasitical on a host of species, never, to my knowledge,
drops an egg in the nest of *M. badius*, unless it be
in a forsaken nest ! Perhaps it will be difficult for
naturalists to believe this ; for if the *M. badius* is so
excessively vigilant and jealous of other birds approaching its nest as to succeed in keeping out the
subtle, silent, grey-plumaged, omnipresent female
M. bonariensis, why does it not also keep off the far
rarer, noisy, bustling, conspicuously coloured *M.
rufoaxillaris*? I cannot say. The only explanation
that has occurred to me is that *M. badius* is sagacious
enough to distinguish the eggs of the common parasite

and throws them out of its nest. But this is scarcely probable, for I have hunted in vain under the trees for the ejected eggs; and I have never found the eggs of *M. badius* with holes pecked in the shells, which would have been the case had a *M. bonariensis* intruded into the nest.

With the results just recorded I felt more than satisfied, though much still remained to be known; and I looked forward to the next summer to work out the rich mine on which I had stumbled by chance. Unhappily when spring came round again ill-health kept me a prisoner in the city, and finding no improvement in my condition, I eventually left Buenos Ayres at the close of the warm season to try whether change of climate would benefit me. Before leaving, however, I spent a few days at home, and saw enough then to satisfy me that my conclusions were correct. Most of the birds had finished breeding, but while examining some nests of *Anumbius* I found one which Bay-wings had tenanted, and which for some reason they had forsaken, leaving *ten* unincubated eggs. They were all like Bay-wings' eggs, but I have no doubt that five of them were eggs of *M. rufo-axillaris*. During my rides in the neighbourhood I also found two flocks of Bay-wings, each composed of several families, and amongst the young birds I noticed several individuals beginning to assume the purple plumage, like those of the previous autumn. I did not think it necessary to shoot more specimens.

The question why *M. badius* permits *M. rufo-axillaris* to use its nest, while excluding the allied parasite *M. bonariensis*, must be answered by future observers; but before passing from this very interesting group (*Molothrus*) I wish to make some general remarks on their habits and their anomalous relations to other species.

It is with a considerable degree of repugnance that we regard the parasitical instinct in birds; the reason it excites such a feeling is manifestly that it presents itself to the mind as—to use the words of a naturalist of the eighteenth century, who was also a theologian and believed the Cuckoo had been created with such a habit—" a monstrous outrage on the maternal affection, one of the first great dictates of nature." An *outrage*, since each creature has been endowed with this all-powerful affection for the preservation of its own, and not another, species; and here we see it, by a subtle process, an unconscious iniquity, turned from its purpose, perverted and made subservient to the very opposing agency against which it was intended as a safeguard! The formation of such an instinct seems indeed like an unforeseen contingency in the system of nature, a malady strengthened, if not induced, by the very laws established for the preservation of health, and which the *vis medicatrix* of nature is incapable of eliminating. Again, the egg of a parasitical species is generally so much larger, differing also in coloration from the eggs it is placed with, whilst there is such an unvarying dissimilarity between the young bird and its living or murdered foster-brothers that, unreasoning as we know instinct, and especially the maternal instinct, to be, we are shocked at so glaring and flagrant an instance of its blind stupidity.

In the competition for place, the struggle for existence, said with reason to be most deadly between such species as are most nearly allied, the operations are imperceptible, and the changes are so gradual that the diminution and final disappearance of one species is never attributed to a corresponding increase in another more favoured species over the same region. It is not as if the regnant species had invaded and seized on the province of another, but appears rather as if they had quietly entered on the possession of an inheritance that was theirs by right. Mighty as are the results worked out by such a process, it is only by a somewhat strained metaphor that it can be called a *struggle*. But even when the war is open and declared, as between a raptorial species and its victims, the former is manifestly driven by necessity, and in this case the species preyed on are endowed with peculiar sagacity to escape its persecutions; so that the war is not one of extermination, but, as in a border war, the invader is satisfied with carrying off the weak and unwary stragglers. Thus the open declared enmity is in reality beneficial to a species; for it is sure to cut off all such individuals as might cause its degeneration. But we can conceive no necessity for such a fatal instinct as that of the Cuckoo and Cow-bird, destructive to such myriads of lives in their beginning. And inasmuch as their preservation is inimical to the species on which they are parasitical, there must also here be a struggle. But what kind of struggle ? not as in other species, where one perishes in the combat that gives greater strength to the victor, but an anomalous struggle in which one of the combatants has made his adversary turn his weapons against himself, and so seems to have an infinite advantage. It is impossible for him to suffer defeat; and yet, to follow out the metaphor, he has so wormed about and interlaced himself with his opponent that as soon as he succeeds in overcoming him he also must inevitably perish. Such a result is perhaps impossible, as there are so many causes operating to check the undue increase of any one species; consequently the struggle, unequal as it appears, must continue for ever. Thus, in whatever way we view the parasitical habit, it appears cruel, treacherous, and vicious in the highest degree. But should we attempt mentally to create a perfect parasitical instinct (that is, one that would be thoroughly efficient with the least possible prejudice to or injustice towards another species ; for the preservation of the species on which the parasite is dependent is necessary to its own) by combining in imagination all known parasitical habits, eliminating every offensive quality or circumstance, and attributing such others in their place as we should think fit, our conception would still probably fall short in simplicity, beauty, and completeness of the actual instinct of *M. rufoaxillaris.* Instead of laying its eggs promiscuously in every receptacle that offers, it selects the nest of a single species ; so that its selective instinct is related to the adaptive resemblance in its eggs and young to those of the species on which it is parasitical. Such an adaptive resemblance could not of course exist if it laid its eggs in the nests of more than one species, and it is certainly a circumstance eminently favourable to preservation. Then, there not being any such incongruity and unfitness as we find in nests into which other parasites intrude, there is no reason here to regard the foster-parents' affection as blind and stupid ; the similarity being close enough to baffle the keenest sagacity. Nor can the instinct here appear in the light of an outrage on the maternal affection ; for the young *M. rufoaxillaris* possesses no advantage over its foster-brothers. It is not endowed with greater strength and voracity to monopolise the attentions of the foster-parent or to eject the real offspring ; but being in every particular precisely like them, it has only an equal chance of being preserved. To this wonderful parasitical instinct we may well apply Darwin's words, when speaking of the architecture of the hive-bee : " Beyond this stage of perfection natural selection could not lead."

RED-BREASTED MARSH-BIRD

Leistes superciliaris

Brownish black; superciliaries pale brown; bend of the wing and body beneath from chin to middle of the belly deep scarlet; bill and legs black; length 7 inches. Female pale brown, variegated with black, faintly touched with red on the breast.

THE most interesting point concerning this species is the very great difference in habits, as well as appearance, existing between the sexes. In form it resembles the Starling of Europe, but is a trifle smaller and has a shorter tail. The male is black, the upper parts faintly mottled with yellowish grey; there is a straw-coloured stripe over the eye; the throat and breast bright crimson. The female is a smaller bird, and in colour dull fulvous grey, mottled with fuscous; the red tint on the breast scarcely perceptible.

These birds are migratory, and appear everywhere in the eastern part of the Argentine country early in October, arriving singly, after which each male takes up a position in a field or open space abounding with coarse grass and herbage, where he spends most of the time perched on the summit of a tall stalk or weed, his glowing crimson bosom showing at a distance like some splendid flower above the herbage. At intervals of two or three minutes he soars vertically up to a height of twenty or twenty-five yards to utter his song, composed of a single long, powerful, and rather musical note, ending with an attempt at a flourish, during which the bird flutters and turns about in the air; then, as if discouraged at his failure, he drops down, emitting harsh guttural chirps, to resume his stand. Meanwhile the female is invisible, keeping closely concealed under the long grass. But at length, attracted perhaps by the bright bosom and aerial music of the male, she occasionally exhibits herself for a few moments, starting up with a wild zigzag flight, like a Snipe flushed from its marsh, and, darting this way and that, presently drops into the grass once more. The moment she appears above the grass the male gives chase, and they vanish from sight together. Thus, while in colour, habits, language, and even in its manner of soaring up like a rocket to let off its curious melody, the male is the most conspicuous of small birds, the female, acted on in an opposite direction by natural selection, has been, so to speak, effaced. While flying they do not look like birds of the same species : the male moves with wings rapidly fluttered, like a Starling, but with a slower, more laborious flight, and without deviating ; the female, in her eccentric movements in the air, reminds one of a large moth, driven from its hiding-place and flying about confused with the glare of noon.

The nest is made of dry grass on the ground, so cunningly concealed that it is difficult to find. The eggs are four, white, spotted with reddish brown. When they have young I have never been able to detect the female flying about in search of food.

All through the summer these birds are solitary, but when migrating in the autumn, though many are seen travelling singly and appear very conspicuous as they fly laboriously in a straight line, at an altitude of about twenty yards from the surface, others are seen making their journey in small flocks or parties composed of six to a dozen individuals. These are the males. The females travel separately, in twos or threes or singly, flying nearer to the earth, with frequent pauses when the wings cease beating, and intervals of gliding, also darting occasionally to one side, as if the bird had suddenly taken fright.

MILITARY STARLING
Trupialis militaris (Linn.)

MILITARY STARLING

Trupialis defilippii

Slightly smaller than last; plumage the same except the under wing-coverts, which are black.

THROUGHOUT the country where this species abounds it is called *Pecho colorado,* which is certainly better than Azara's barbarous, if picturesque, name of *Degollado*; but no happier name than *militaris* could have been invented for it, by which it was formerly known to naturalists; and though it was given to the bird merely on account of the red breast, and was therefore equally applicable to all the red-breasted species on the globe, in this case it accidentally seemed to describe a peculiar habit of the bird, as well as its bright livery.

In size, form, gait, flight, language, and colour the present bird very closely resembles the Patagonian Starling; but the crimson on the breast is brighter and the upper parts are darker. Its nesting habits are also like those of the southern bird; the number and colour of the eggs being the same in both species. One trivial difference in habit is that De Filippi's Starling occasionally soars up a few yards into the air when uttering its song. It inhabits the moist grassy pampas in the southern part of the Buenos Ayrean province, and is there abundant and unites in large flocks. At the approach of the cold season there is a general movement northwards of the birds, which does not, however, extend far, as the birds, although strong fliers, travel slowly and in a peculiar manner; it is in this season when the birds are seen moving in large flocks, that the name of Military Starling strikes one as being peculiarly appropriate.

They do not journey through the air like other migrants, but move over the ground, when the flock, composed of four or five hundred to a thousand or more individuals, is extended so as to present a very long front, and at intervals the hindmost birds fly over the others and alight just in front of them : the long front, the precision of their movements, and their scarlet bosoms all turned one way, suggest the idea of a disciplined army on its march.

They never perch on trees, but frequently alight on the roof of a rancho or other elevation affording a secure footing. They are tame birds and fly reluctantly ; when approached they usually crouch down, hiding their crimson bosoms, and remain motionless in order to escape observation. In disposition they are peaceful, and so fond of society that when one becomes separated from his fellows he will unite with birds of another kind, even with Plovers or Tyrant-birds.

On the great monotonous plains, where most of the small birds are grey- or brown-plumaged, and in winter when there are no flowers to satisfy the desire of the eye for bright colour, it is delightful while travelling to meet with an army of these Starlings : their crimson bosoms, less bright than the hues of some tropical species, seem then to glow with a strange splendour on the sombre green of earth, and the sight produces an exhilarating effect on the mind.

BLACK-CROWNED TYRANT

Tænioptera coronata

Above cinereous; rounded summit of head black, broad front and band encircling the black of the head white; wings blackish, upper coverts cinereous, edgings of middle and greater coverts and of outer secondaries whitish; tail blackish, margins of outer webs of external tail feathers white; beneath white; under wing-coverts and a large portion of the inner webs of the remiges, except of the two outer primaries, white; bill and feet black; length 7.8 inches.

IN this species the sexes are alike. The crown is black and composed of loose feathers; the forehead, and a broad line over the eye which extends nearly round the head, also all the under plumage, pure white; neck and back clear grey; quills black.

This Tyrant is a solitary bird, though often many individuals are found within call of each other, and they sometimes even unite in a loose flock. It is found throughout the Argentine country, ranging south to the Rio Negro, in Patagonia, but abounds most on the Buenos-Ayrean pampas, where it performs a partial migration. Most of the *Tænioptera* seek their food by preference on the bare level ground, or where the vegetation is most scanty. This species varies somewhat in habits, and seldom runs on the ground, and chiefly inhabits the desert plains, where the large grasses flourish. On one occasion when I was with an expedition on the pampas for several weeks, every day a number of these birds would gather and follow us; perched here and there on the tall grasses with their bosoms towards us, they often looked at a distance like large white flowers. Old gauchos have told me that fifty years ago they were abundant all over the pampas, but have disappeared wherever the giant grasses have been eaten down and have given place to a different vegetation.

Their note is a long, low whistle, the usual language of the *Tænioptera*; but in this species it is very like a human whistle, on account of which the bird is named *Boyero* (ox-driver) on the pampas. One severe winter great numbers of them appeared in the neighbourhood of Buenos Ayres, and it was amusing to see the dogs thrown into a great state of excitement by the low whistling notes heard perpetually from all sides. Every few moments they would start up and stare about them to ascertain where the deceptive call came from, and in spite of many disappointments they would occasionally all rush away, loudly barking, into the plantation, convinced that some person there was whistling to call them.

The Black-Crown makes a somewhat shallow nest in a bush or large clump of grass, and lays four white eggs, with large dark red spots, chiefly at the big end.

I cannot refrain from quoting a passage from Mr. Barrows' paper, descriptive of the lively temper and habits of this bird :

" This species often persecutes smaller birds in a way which seems to imply pure love of mischief. One afternoon in July, when the river had fallen some feet after an unusual rise, I was walking along the lines of drift left by the falling water, and watching the different birds which were picking up insects or other food from the wind-rows. A score or two of the little chestnut-backed *Centrites* were running about, and here and there a *Tænioptera* was looking quietly on. Suddenly I heard a chirp of distress, and looking up saw one of these small birds apparently making every effort to escape from a *Tænioptera*, which was following in full chase. The two birds were hardly a length apart and both going at full speed, doubling and dodging in a way that would have done credit to a bat. The chase lasted perhaps for half a minute, when the smaller bird alighted, and at once the other also alighted and began running about unconcernedly and picking up food. But the instant the smaller one made a start his enemy was at his heels (or more properly his tail) again, and he was forced to alight. This was repeated so often that I was on the point of shooting the pursuer, when, without any notice, he flew quietly off, and resumed his usual demeanour. It looked like a case of simple spite, for even if there were twenty other birds about, one seemed to be followed without regard to the rest."

I have often watched *Tæniopteræ* of different species, also *Myiotheretes rufiventris*, behaving in a similar way, and agree with Mr. Barrows that it is " an *amusement* in which the larger bird indulges simply for the pleasure derived from the exercise of his power."

BIENTEVEO TYRANT
Pitangus bolivianus (Lafr.)

BIENTEVEO TYRANT

Pitangus bolivianus

Above brown ; head black ; front, superciliaries, and line round
the nape white ; large vertical crest yellow, tipped with black ; wings
and tail brown with rufous margins ; beneath sulphur-yellow, inner
margins of wing- and tail-feathers pale rufous ; bill and feet black ;
length 9 inches.

THE Bienteveo is in its habits the most interesting
member of the Tyrannine family. It would be
difficult to find two species more dissimilar in disposition than are the Silverbill, already described,
and the Bienteveo ; the former being like an auto-
maton, having only a few set motions, gestures, and
instincts, while the other is versatile in an extraordinary degree, and seems to have studied to
advantage the various habits of the Kestrel, Flycatcher, Kingfisher, Vulture, and fruit-eating Thrush ;
and when its weapons prove weak it supplements
them with its cunning. How strange it is that these
two species, mentally as widely separated as the
Humming-bird and Crow, should be members of
the same family !

The Bienteveo has a wide range in South America,
and inhabits the whole of the Argentine country
down to Buenos Ayres, where it is very common.
It is resident and lives in pairs, the sexes being always
faithful. The body is stout, somewhat large for a
Tyrant-bird ; the length being nine and a half
inches, including the beak, which is a little over an
inch in length. The wings are blunt and comparatively short, measuring when spread fourteen inches.
The head is large, and a broad black band extends
from the beak its entire length, and above this is
a pure white stripe ; the crown is black, concealing
in its loose abundant feathers a brilliant yellow crest,

which shows only when the bird is excited. The
upper plumage, including wings and tail, is pale
brown; the entire under-surface sulphur yellow.
In both sexes the plumage is alike.

In Buenos Ayres the Bienteveo is found in every
orchard and plantation; it is familiar with man and
invariably greets his approach with loud notes—
especially with a powerful three-syllabled cry, in
which people fancy there is a resemblance to the
words *Bién-te-veo* (" I see you well "); while its
big head and beak, and strongly contrasted colours,
especially the black and white head-stripes, seem to
give it a wonderfully knowing look, as it turns its
head from side to side to examine the intruder. It
is a loud-voiced garrulous bird, and has a great range
of sounds, from grating screams to long, clear, almost
mellow call-notes. It has one pretty habit, which
brings out an agreeable feature in its character.
Though the male and female are greatly attached,
they do not go afield to hunt in company, like the
Short-winged Tyrant, but separate to meet again
at intervals during the day. One of a couple (say
the female) returns to the trees where they are
accustomed to meet, and after a time, becoming im-
patient or anxious at the delay of her consort, utters
a very long, clear call-note. He is perhaps three or
four fields away, watching for a frog beside a pool,
or beating, harrier-like, over a thistle-bed, but
he hears the note and presently responds with one
of equal power. Then perhaps for half an hour, at
intervals of half a minute, the birds answer each
other, though the powerful call of the one must
interfere with his hunting. At length he returns;
then the two birds, perched close together, with their
yellow bosoms almost touching, crests elevated, and
beating the branch with their wings, scream their

loudest notes in concert—a confused jubilant noise
that rings through the whole plantation. Their joy
at meeting is patent, and their action corresponds to
the warm embrace of a loving human couple.

I have frequently stood for the space of half an
hour concealed amongst the trees where a Bienteveo
was calling to her mate, cheered at intervals by the
far-off faint response, for the pleasure of witnessing
in the end the joyful reunion of the two birds.

Except when breeding the Bienteveo is a peaceful
bird, never going out of its way to make gratuitous
attacks on individuals of its own or of other species ;
but in the pursuit of its prey it is cunning, bold, and
fierce. Like the true Tyrant-birds it preys a great
deal on large insects when they are abundant in the
warm season, and is frequently seen catching its prey
in the air. A large beetle or grasshopper it invariably
beats against a branch before devouring it. But even
in summer, when insect prey is most abundant, it
prefers a more substantial diet whenever such is to
be had. It frequently carries off the fledglings of
the smaller birds from their nests, in the face of the
brave defence often made by the parents. It is also
fond of fishing, and may be seen perched by the hour
on a bank or overhanging branch beside a stream,
watching the water like a Kingfisher, and at intervals
dashing down to capture the small fry. In shallow
pools, where there are tadpoles and other prey, the
Bienteveo does not mind getting a little wet, but
alights in the water and stands belly-deep watching
for its prey. I have seen a Bienteveo standing in the
water in the midst of a flock of Glossy Ibises. They
are often seen, as Darwin remarks, hovering like a
Kestrel over the grass and then dashing down to
seize their prey. Small snakes, frogs, mice, and
lizards all minister to its appetite, and with a capture

of this kind it invariably flies to the nearest stone or
branch, against which it beats out the life of its
victim before devouring it.   I once saw one fly out
of some weeds carrying a little wriggling glass-
snake about eight inches long in its beak.   Alighting
on a gate it proceeded to kill its capture, and at the
first blow on the wood the snake flew into two
pieces.   A mouse gives it a great deal of trouble,
for after it has been killed it cannot be devoured
until reduced by repeated blows to a soft pulp,
after which it is with great labour pulled to pieces
and eaten.   Snails and *Ampullariæ* are also pounded
until the shell breaks.   In spring they sometimes
join the train of Hooded Gulls, Guira Cuckoos,
Cow-birds, and various other kinds which follow
the plough to pick up worms and larvæ; but on the
ground the Bienteveo is awkward in its motions, for
it cannot run like the Tyrant-birds of terrestrial
habits, but only hops.   At estancia houses, when a
cow is slaughtered, it comes in with the fowls,
Carrion Hawks, and dogs, for small pickings, being
very fond of fresh meat.   It is a common thing to
see a Bienteveo following a rural butcher's cart, and
waiting for an opportunity to dash in and carry off
any small piece of meat or fat it is able to detach.
In the autumn they feed very much on ripe fruit,
preferring grapes, which they can swallow whole,
and figs, which are soft and easily devoured.

In its nidification the Bienteveo also departs widely
from the, so to speak, traditional habits of its congeners; for whereas most Tyrants make shallow
nests, this species makes a very big elaborate domed
structure, and sometimes takes five or six weeks to
complete it.   It is placed in a tree, without any
attempt at concealment, and is about a foot deep
and eight or nine inches broad, and composed of a

variety of soft materials, chiefly wool. The entrance is placed near the top. Outside, the nest has a very disorderly appearance, as there are always long straws and sometimes rags hanging down; the cavity is deeply lined with feathers, and is the *hottest* nest I know. The eggs are five, very long, pointed, cream-coloured, and spotted, chiefly at the larger end, with chocolate and purple.

They are bold in defence of their nest; one pair which bred annually in my orchard always attacked me with the greatest fury whenever I ventured near the peach-tree in which they had their big nest of wool, darting down repeatedly and striking my head with beak and wings.

RED OVEN-BIRD

Furnarius rufus (Gm.)

OVEN-BIRD

Furnarius rufus

Above earthy brown, with a slight rufescent tinge, wing-feathers blackish, margined with pale brown; whole of the outer secondaries pale brown, like the back; tail and upper tail-coverts bright ferruginous brown; below white, breast and flanks and under wing-coverts pale sandy-brown; under surface of the wing with a broad sandy bar across the basal portion; length 8 to 9 inches.

THE Red Oven-bird is an extremely well-known species in Argentina, and, where found, a great favourite on account of its familiarity with man, its loud, ringing, cheerful voice, and its wonderful mud nest, which it prefers to build near a human habitation, often on a cornice, a projecting beam, or on the roof of the house itself.

It is a stout little bird, with a slender, slightly-curved beak nearly an inch in length, and strong legs suited to its terrestrial habits. The upper plumage is uniform rufous-brown in colour, brightest on the tail; the under surface very light brown. It ranges throughout the Argentine Republic to Bahia Blanca in the south, and is usually named *Hornero* or *Casera* (Oven-bird or Housekeeper); in Brazil, *João de los barrios* (John of the Mud-puddles) or John Clay, as Richard Burton translates it. In Paraguay and Corrientes it is *Alonzo Garcia* or else *Alonzito*, the affectionate diminutive. Azara, that sensible naturalist, losing his mind for a moment, solemnly says that he can give no reason for such a name! He might have found the reason in his own country in Europe, where as a boy he knew the wild bird life and where a bird which inspires affectionate admiration in the country people is sometimes called by a human name. As a rule it is a Christian name,

as in the case of our Robin, in England, which in
Norway is called Peter, and our Jack—we have
several Jacks—and our Margaret or Mag, and our
Peggy and Kitty and Jenny. The *Alonzo Garcia* is
specially favoured in having both a Christian and
a surname. I have often been assured by natives that
the *Hornero* is a religious bird and always suspends
his labours on a Sunday and on all holy days.

It is resident, pairs for life, and finds its food,
which consists of larvæ and worms, exclusively on
the ground. It delights in open places, where it can
move freely about on the ground; and is partial
to court-yards, clean garden-walks, etc., where, with
head thrown back and bosom prominent, it struts
along with an air of great gravity, lifting its foot high
at each step, and holding it suspended for a moment
in the air before setting it firmly down. I once saw
one fly down on to a narrow plank about ten feet
long lying out on the wet grass; it walked gravely
to the end of the plank, then turned, and deliberately
walked back to the other end, and so on for about
twenty times, appearing to take the greatest pleasure
in the mere act of promenading on a smooth, level
surface. When disturbed, the Oven-bird has a loud
monotonous note of alarm or curiosity, which never
fails to bring all its fellows within hearing distance
to the spot. The movements of a fox, weasel, or cat
in a plantation can always be known from the noisy
turmoil among the Oven-birds. At frequent intervals
during the day the male and female meet and express
their joy in clear, resonant notes sung in concert—a
habit common to a very large number of Dendrocolaptine birds, including, I think, all those species
which pair for life. In a majority of species this
vocal performance merely consists of a succession
of confused notes or cries, uttered with great spirit

and emphasis ; in the Oven-bird it has developed
into a kind of harmonious singing. Thus, the first
bird, on the appearance of its mate flying to the place
of meeting, emits loud, measured notes, sometimes
a continuous trilling note with a somewhat hollow,
metallic sound ; but immediately on the other bird
joining, this introductory passage is changed to rapid
triplets, strongly accented on the first and last notes,
while the second bird utters a series of loud measured
notes perfectly according with the triplets of the
first. While thus singing they stand facing each
other, their necks outstretched, wings hanging, and
tails spread, the first bird trembling with its rapid
utterances, the second beating on the branch with
its wings. The finale consists of three or four notes
uttered by the second bird alone, and becoming
successively louder and more piercing until the end.
There is an infinite variety in the tone in which different couples sing, also in the order in which the
different notes are uttered, and even the same couple
do not repeat their duet in precisely the same way ;
but it is always a rhythmical and, to some extent,
an harmonious performance, and as the voices have
a ringing, joyous character, it produces a pleasing
effect on the mind.

In favourable seasons the Oven-birds begin building in the autumn, and the work is resumed during
the winter whenever there is a spell of mild, wet
weather. Some of their structures are finished early
in winter, others not until spring, everything de-
pending on the weather and the condition of the
birds. In cold, dry weather, and when food is scarce,
they do not work at all. The site chosen is a stout
horizontal branch, or the top of a post, and they also
frequently build on the roof of a house ; and sometimes, but rarely, on the ground. The material used

is mud, with the addition of horsehair or slender fibrous rootlets, which make the structure harder and prevent it from cracking. I have frequently seen a bird, engaged in building, first pick up a thread or hair, then repair to a puddle, where it was worked into a pellet of mud about the size of a filbert, then carried to the nest. When finished the structure is shaped outwardly like a baker's oven, only with a deeper and narrower entrance.

It is always placed very conspicuously, and with the entrance facing a building, if one be near, or if at a roadside it looks toward the road ; the reason for this being, no doubt, that the bird keeps a cautious eye on the movements of people near it while building. and so leaves the nest opened and unfinished on that side until the last, and there the entrance is necessarily formed. When the structure has assumed the globular form with only a narrow opening, the wall on one side is curved inwards, reaching from the floor to the dome, and at the inner extremity an aperture is left to admit the bird to the interior or second chamber, in which the eggs are laid. A man's hand fits easily into the first or entrance chamber, but cannot be twisted about so as to reach the eggs in the interior cavity, the entrance being so small and high up. The interior is lined with dry, soft grass, and five white pear-shaped eggs are laid. The oven is a foot or more in diameter, and is sometimes very massive, weighing eight or nine pounds, and so strong that, unless loosened by the swaying of the branch, it often remains unharmed for two or three years. The birds incubate by turns, and when one returns from the feeding-ground it sings its loud notes, on which the sitting bird rushes forth to join in the joyous chorus, and then flies away, the other taking its place on the eggs. The young are exceedingly garrulous, and when only half-fledged may be heard practising trills and duets in their secure oven, in shrill tremulous voices, which change to the usual hunger-cry of young birds when the parent enters with food. After leaving the nest, the old and young birds live for two or three months together, only one brood being raised in each year. A new oven is built every year, and I have more than once seen a second oven built on the top of the first, when this has been placed very advantageously, as on a projection and against a wall.

A very curious thing occurred at the estancia house of a neighbour of mine in Buenos Ayres one spring. A pair of Oven-birds built their oven on a beam-end projecting from the wall of a rancho. One morning one of the birds was found caught in a steel trap placed the evening before for rats, and both of its legs were crushed above the knee. On being liberated it flew up to and entered the oven, where it bled to death, no doubt, for it did not come out again. Its mate remained two days, calling incessantly, but there were no other birds of its kind in the place, and it eventually disappeared. Three days later it returned with a new mate, and immediately the two birds began carrying pellets of mud to the oven, with which they plastered up the entrance. Afterwards they built a second oven, using the sepulchre of the dead bird for its foundation, and here they reared their young. My neighbour, an old native, had watched the birds from the time the first oven was begun, feeling greatly interested in their diligent ways, and thinking their presence at his house a good omen; and it was not strange that, after witnessing the entombment of the one that died, he was more convinced than ever that the little House-builders are "pious birds."

RUSH-LOVING SPINE-TAIL

Phlœocryptes melanops

Above, forehead brown, crown blackish, broad superciliaries buffy white; upper half of back black; marked with a few grey stripes; lower back and rump, also sides of back and neck, light brown; wings blackish, mottled with light chestnut on the coverts; and a broad band of the same colour occupying the basal half of the wing-feathers; tail blackish, the two middle feathers brownish grey, the others slightly tipped with the same colour; beneath white, more or less tinged on the throat, flanks, and under tail-coverts with pale brown; under wing-coverts fulvous; length 5.8 inches.

THIS is one of our few strictly migratory species in the family *Dendrocolaptidæ*. Probably it winters in South Brazil, as in the northern parts of the Argentine country it is said to be a summer visitor. On the pampas it appears in September, and all at once becomes very abundant in the rush-beds growing in the water, where alone it is found. The migration no doubt is very extensive, for in spring I found it very abundant in the rush-beds in the Rio Negro valley, and Durnford met with it much further south on the river Sanguelen, a tributary of the Chupat. Migratory birds are, as a rule, very little given to wandering; that is to say, they do not go much beyond the limits of the little coppice, reed-bed, or spot of ground which they make their summer home, and this species is no exception. It spends the warm season secluded in its rush-bed: and when disturbed flies with great reluctance, fluttering feebly away to a distance of a few yards, and then dropping into the rushes again, apparently quite incapable of a sustained flight. How a bird so feeble on the wing, and retiring in its habits, is able to perform a long annual migration, when in traversing vast tracts of open country it must be in great peril from rapacious

kinds, is a great mystery. No doubt many perish
while travelling; but there is this circumstance in
their favour: an incredible number of birds of
various kinds, many as weak and exposed to attack
as the *Phlœocryptes*, migrate simultaneously; Hawks
are but thinly scattered along their route, and as a
rule these birds feed only once or twice a day, if the
meals are large enough to fill the stomach, so that
while the Hawk is inactive, digesting his meal,
thousands of migrants have sped by on their journey
and are beyond his reach for ever.

The Spine-tail seldom ventures out of its rush-
bed, but is occasionally seen feeding in the grass and
herbage a few yards removed from the water. Its
language is peculiar, this being a long cicada-like
note, followed by a series of sounds like smart taps
on a piece of dry wood. It frequents the same places
as the small Many-coloured Tyrant (*Cyanotis azaræ*),
and these little neighbours, being equally inquisitive,
whenever a person approaches the rushes often
emerge together, one uttering wooden-sounding
creaks and raps, the other liquid gurgling notes—
a little brown bird and a little bird with many bright
colours, both, in very different tones, demanding to
know the reason of the intrusion.

The nest is a very wonderful structure, and is
usually attached to three upright stems; it is domed,
oval-shaped, about nine inches deep, and the small
circular aperture which is close to the top is protected
by a sloping tile-like projection. It is built of tough
grass-leaves, which are apparently first daubed with
wet clay and then ingeniously woven in, with the
addition, I think, of some kind of mucilage: the
whole nest is, when finished, light but very strong,
and impervious to wet. Until the rushes die and
drop the nest remains securely fastened to them,

and in winter affords a safe and comfortable retreat to the small, rush- or reed-frogs, of which sometimes as many as three or four are found living in one nest. The interior is very thickly lined with feathers ; the eggs are three, pear-shaped, and a bright, beautiful blue colour, sometimes with a slight greenish tinge.

The bird is so abundant in extensive marshes that I have on several occasions, during a half-day's ramble, found as many as forty or fifty nests, some-times a dozen or more being placed close together, but I have never taken more than three eggs from one nest. I mention this because I have seen it stated that four or five eggs are sometimes found.

I trust that no reader of this sketch imagines that I robbed all the eggs contained in so many nests. I did nothing so barbarous, although it is perhaps " prattling out of fashion " to say so ; but with the destructive, useless egg-collecting passion I have no sympathy. By bending the pliant rushes down-wards the eggs can be made to roll out into the hand ; and all those which I thus took out to count were put back in their wonderful cradles. I had a special object in examining so many nests. A gaucho boy once brought me a nest which had a small circular *stopper*, made of the same texture as the body of the nest, attached to the aperture at the *side* and when swung round into it fitting it as perfectly as the lid of the trap-door spider fits the burrow. I have no doubt that it was used to close the nest when the bird was away, perhaps to prevent the intrusion of reed-frogs or of other small birds ; but I have never found another nest like it, nor have I heard of one being found by any one else ; and that one nest, with its perfectly-fitting stopper, has been a puzzle to my mind ever since I saw it.

HUDSON'S SPINE-TAIL

Synallaxis hudsoni

Above fulvous brown, mottled with black, each feather being marked
with a large black spot; on the upper part of the back the feathers
are faintly edged with whitish grey; wings blackish, basal halves of
feathers pale clear brown, forming a transverse bar, the terminal part
of the feathers slightly edged on the outer webs and tips with ochraceous;
tail blackish, the outer pair of rectrices and broad tips of the next
two pairs on each side very pale brown, the two middle feathers broadly
margined on both webs with pale greyish brown; beneath pale ochraceous brown, with a pale sulphur-yellowish gular spot; flanks with a
few black marks; under wing-coverts light cinnamon; length 7.8 inches.

THIS Spine-tail, which Sclater named after me, is
the Argentine representative of *S. humicola* of Chili.
It is common on the pampas, and is sometimes
called by the gauchos *Tíru-ríru del campo*, on
account of its resemblance in the upper plumage
and in language to *Anumbius acuticaudatus*, which
is named *Tíru-ríru* in imitation of its call-note.
The addition of *del campo* signifies that it is a bird
of the open country. It is, in fact, found exclusively
on the grassy pampas, never perching on trees, and
in habits is something like a Pipit, usually being
taken for one when first seen. It is quite common
everywhere on the pampas, and specimens have also
been obtained in Cordova, Uruguay, and Patagonia.

This Spine-tail is resident, solitary, and extremely
timid and stealthy in its movements, living always
on the ground among the long grass and cardoon-
thistles. At times its inquisitiveness overcomes its
timidity, and the bird then darts up three or four
yards into the air, and jerking its tail remains some
moments poised aloft with breast towards the intruder, emitting sharp little notes of alarm, after
which it darts down again and disappears in the grass.

This is a habit common to most Pipits. When driven up it has a wild zigzag flight, and after reaching a considerable height in the air darts down again with astonishing swiftness, and comes back to the very spot from which it rose. It is, however, incapable of sustained flight, and after being flushed two or three times refuses to rise again. In spring the male perches on the summit of a cardoon-bush, or other slight elevation, and at regular intervals utters a pleasing and melancholy kind of song or call, which can be heard distinctly at a distance of a thousand yards, composed of four long clear plaintive notes, increasing in strength, and succeeded by a falling trill. When approached it becomes silent, and dropping to the ground conceals itself in the grass. Under a cardoon-bush or tussock it scoops out a slight hollow in the ground, and builds over this a dome of fine dry grass, leaving a small aperture arched like the door of a baker's oven. The bed is lined with dry powdered horse-dung, and the eggs are five, bluntly pointed and of a very pale buff colour. The interior of the nest is so small that when the five young birds are fledged they appear to be packed together very closely, so that it is difficult to conceive how the parent bird passes in and out.

The nest is always very cunningly concealed, and I have often spent days searching in a patch of cardoon-bushes where the birds were breeding without being able to find it. Something more will be said about the nesting-habits of this species in the account of the Carrion-hawk, *Milvago chimango.*

FIREWOOD-GATHERER

Anumbius acuticaudatus

Above earthy brown, forehead chestnut, superciliaries white; head, neck, and back marked with black striations; primaries blackish, secondaries pale chestnut-brown; tail black, all the feathers except the middle pair broadly tipped with cream-colour; beneath pale ochraceous brown, white on the throat, the white bordered on each side by numerous black spots; length 8.5 inches.

THIS is a common and very well-known species throughout the Argentine country and Patagonia, also in Uruguay and Paraguay, and is variously called *Espinero* (Thorn-bird), *Tiru-riru*, in imitation of its note, and *Añumbi* (the Guarani name); but its best-known name is *Leñatero*, or " Firewood-gatherer," from the quantity of sticks which it collects for building purposes.

The Firewood-gatherer is a resident in Argentina, and pairs for life. Sometimes the young birds remain with their parents for a period of three or four months, all the family going about and feeding in company, and roosting together in the old nest. The nest and the tree where it is placed are a favourite resort all the year round. Here the birds sit perched a great deal, and repeat at intervals a song or call, composed of four or five loud ticking chirps, followed by a long trilling note. They feed exclusively on the ground, where they creep about, carrying the body horizontally and intently searching for insects. When disturbed they hurry to their usual refuge, rapidly beating their very feeble wings, and expanding the broad acuminated tail like a fan. When the male and female meet at their nest, after a brief separation, they sing their notes in concert, as if rejoicing over their safe reunion; but they seldom separate, and

72

Azara says that when one incubates, the other sits at the entrance to the nest, and that when one returns to the nest with food for the young the other accompanies it, though it has found nothing to carry.

To build, the *Añumbi* makes choice of an isolated tree in an open situation, and prefers a dwarf tree with very scanty foliage ; for small projecting twigs and leaves hinder the worker when carrying up sticks. This is a most laborious operation, as the sticks are large and the bird's flight is feeble. If the tree is to its liking, it matters not how much exposed to the winds it may be, or how close to a human habitation, for the bird is utterly unconcerned by the presence of man. I have frequently seen a nest in a shade or ornamental tree within ten yards of the main entrance to a house ; and I have also seen several on the tall upright stakes of a horse-corral, and the birds working quietly, with a herd of half-wild horses rushing round the enclosure beneath them, pursued by the men with lassoes. The bird uses large sticks for building, and drops a great many ; frequently as much fallen material as would fill a barrow lies under the tree. The fallen stick is not picked up again, as the bird could not rise vertically with its load, and is not intelligent enough, I suppose, to recover the fallen stick and to carry it away thirty yards from the tree and then rise obliquely. It consequently goes far afield in quest of a fresh one, and having got one to its liking, carefully takes it up exactly by the middle, and, carrying it like a balancing-pole, returns to the nest, where, if one end happens to hit against a pro-jecting twig, it drops like the first. The bird is not discouraged, but, after a brief interview with its mate, flies cheerfully away to gather more wood.

Durnford writes wonderingly of the partiality for building in poplar trees shown by this bird in Buenos Ayres, and says that in a tall tree the nest is sometimes placed sixty or seventy feet above the ground, and that the bird almost invariably rises with a stick at such a distance from the tree as to be able just to make the nest, but that sometimes failing it alights further down, and then climbs up the twigs with its stick. He attributes the choice of the tall poplar to *ambition*; but the *Añumbi* has really a much simpler and lowlier motive. In the rich Buenos-Ayrean soil all trees have a superabundance of foliage, and in the slim Lombardy poplar alone can the nest be placed where the bird can reach it laden with building-material, without coming in contact with long projecting twigs.

The nest of the *Añumbi* is about two feet in depth, and from ten to twelve inches in diameter, and rests in an oblique position amongst the branches. The entrance is at the top, and a crooked or spiral passage-way leads down to the lower extremity, where the breeding chamber is situated ; this is lined with wool and soft grass, and five white eggs are laid, varying considerably in form, some being much more sharply pointed than others.

The nest, being so secure and comfortable an abode, is greatly coveted by several other species of birds to breed in ; but on this subject I have already spoken in the account of the genus *Molothrus*. When deprived of their nest, the birds immediately set to work to make a new one ; but often enough without being ejected from the first they build a second nest, sometimes demolishing the first work to use the materials. I watched one pair make three nests before laying ; another pair made two nests, and after the second was completed they returned to the first and there elected to remain. Two or three nests are sometimes seen on one tree, and Azara says he has seen as many as six. Mr. Barrows observed the bird at Concepcion, where it is very common, and writes that in that district the nest is sometimes four feet long with an average diameter of two feet, and that the same nest in some cases is used for several seasons successively ; also that several nests are sometimes joined together and all occupied at the same time.

LAUGHING CACHALOTE

Homorus gutturalis

Nearly uniform earthy grey, faintly tinged with olivaceous brown above, and much paler beneath; lores and upper part of throat pure white, lower part of throat black, or white and black mixed; under wing-coverts white, faintly tinged with pale cinnamon; beak and feet bluish grey; length 9.4 inches.

I FOUND this bird quite common on the dry open plains in the neighbourhood of the Rio Negro in Patagonia. In size, form, and crest it is like the northern Cachalote, but has a white throat, while the rest of the plumage is of a pale earthy brown instead of rufous. Like the Rufous Cachalote it is also shy in disposition, and, being so dull in colour and without the bright beak and eye tints, has not the bold, striking appearance of that species; still I do not think any ornithologist can meet with it and fail to be strongly impressed with its personality, if such a word can be applied to a bird.

Dendrocolaptine birds are, as a rule, builders of big nests and very noisy; *H. gutturalis* is, I believe, the loudest screamer and greatest builder of the family. Male and female live together in the same locality all the year; the young, when able to fly, remain with their parents till the breeding-season, so that the birds are found occasionally in pairs, but more frequently in families of five or six individuals. When feeding they scatter about, each bird attaching itself to a large bush, scraping and prodding for insects about the roots; and at intervals one of the old birds, ascending a bush, summons the others with loud shrill cries, on which they all hurry to the place of meeting, and from the summits of the bushes burst forth in a piercing chorus, which sounds at a distance like screams of hysterical laughter. At one place where I spent some months, there were some bushes over a mile and a quarter from the house I lived in, where these birds used to hold frequent meetings, and in that still atmosphere I could distinctly hear their extravagant cries at that distance. After each performance they pursue each other, passing from bush to bush with a wild jerky flight, and uttering harsh excited notes.

They select a low, strong, wide-spreading bush to build in; the nest, which is made of stout sticks, is perfectly spherical and four to five feet deep, the chamber inside being very large. The opening is at the side, near the top, and is approached by a narrow arched gallery, neatly made of slender sticks resting along a horizontal branch, and about fourteen inches long. This peculiar entrance no doubt prevents the intrusion of snakes and small mammals. The structure differs from all the domed nests of other species of Woodhewers in the spaciousness of the cavity where the eggs are laid. The dome removed, an eagle or vulture could breed in it quite comfortably. So strongly made is the nest that I have stood on the dome of one and stamped on it with my heavy boots without injuring it in the least, and to demolish one I had to force my gun barrel into it, then prize it up by portions. I examined about a dozen of these enormous structures, but they were all met with before or after the laying season, so that I did not see the eggs.

GALLITO (Little Cock)

Rhinocrypta lanceolata, Geoffa.

LITTLE COCK

Rhinocrypta lanceolata

Above, head and upper neck reddish brown with a fine white shaft-stripe on each feather, the stripes being most conspicuous on the crest-feathers; lower neck, back, rump, and wings greyish olive; tail blackish; beneath, throat and upper part of breast grey, becoming pure white on the middle of the belly; sides of belly and flanks bright chestnut; lower part of belly and flanks and under tail-coverts like the back; bill horn-colour, feet black; length 9 inches.

THE last Passerine species to be described is the only one known to me belonging to the singular South American Family, *Pteroptochidæ*. They are mostly natives of Chili and the south-western extremity of the South American continent, but have representatives in the Andes of Ecuador and Columbia and the high plateau of Central Brazil.

The vernacular name *Gallito*, or " Little Cock," by which this species is familiarly known in Patagonia, cannot fail to strike every one who sees the bird as appropriate, for it struts and runs on the ground with tail erect, looking wonderfully like a minute domestic fowl. In the neighbourhood of Carmen, on the Rio Negro, it is very abundant, and when I went there its loud deep chirrup, heard from every side in the thicket, quickly arrested my attention, just as the perpetual chirping of the Sparrows did when I first landed in England. In the interior of the country it is not nearly so abundant, so that man's presence has probably in some way affected it favourably. Its habits amuse and baffle a person anxious to make its acquaintance; for it scarcely possesses the faculty of flight, and cannot be driven up, but it is so easily alarmed, so swift of foot, and so fond of concealment, that it is most difficult to catch a sight of it. At the same time it is extremely inquisitive, and no sooner does it spy an intruder in the bush than the warning note is sounded, whereupon every bird within hearing hops up into a thick thorn-bush, where it utters every three or four seconds a loud hollow chirp, and at intervals a violent scolding cry, several times repeated. When approached they all scuttle away, masked by the bushes, with amazing swiftness, to take refuge at a distance, where the loud protest is again resumed; but when the pursuer gives up the pursuit in disgust and turns away, they immediately follow him, so that he is perpetually encircled with the same ring of angry sound, moving with him, coming no nearer and never allowing its cause to be seen.

On three or four occasions I have seen one rise from the ground and fly several yards with a feeble fluttering flight; but when closely pursued in an open place they seem incapable of rising. They generally fly down from the top of a bush, but always ascend it by hopping from twig to twig.

The nest is made in the centre of a thorny bush two or three feet from the ground; and is round and domed, with a small aperture at the side, and built entirely of fine dry grass. The eggs are four in number and pure white.

GLITTERING HUMMING-BIRD

Chlorostilbon splendidus

Head, upper parts, and wing-coverts golden bronze, inclining to
green on upper tail-coverts; wings purplish brown; tail black
glossed with green; throat and breast glittering emerald-green; beak
bright red; length 3.5 inches. Female bronze-green above and grey
beneath.

THE *Trochilidæ*, or Humming-birds, a distinctly
South American form, are one of the most
numerous families of birds on the globe,
numbering over 400 known species, and ranging over
the entire continent down to Tierra del Fuego. How
surprising then to find that of this multitude of species
no more than about a dozen are found in the entire
Argentine country! It only adds to the surprise when
it is found that humming-birds of these few species
are common enough throughout the country. Even
on the almost treeless grassy pampas of Buenos Ayres
which are unsuited to the habits of this feathered
forest sprite, one species at all events is found everywhere. Personally I was acquainted with only
three species, and I recall that when living on the
open pampas, every season when the white acacia
at my home was in flower we had an invasion of
Humming-birds. The plantation was divided by
avenues of large acacia trees, about a thousand
in all, and as long as the blossoms lasted the little
glittering birds were to be seen all over the place,
in almost every tree, revelling in the fragrant sweetness; but no sooner were the flowers faded than
they were gone, and thereafter two or three pairs
only remained to breed and spend the summer months
in the plantation. All these birds were of one species
—the Glittering Humming-bird, but on going a few

miles from home to the marsh and forest on the low shores of the Plata river I would find the other two species. I spent a summer, bird-watching, in a herdsman's hut in the marshy forest and used to go out at sunset to a small open space overgrown with viper's-bugloss in flower. There is no flower the Humming-bird likes so well, and he is most busy feeding just before dark. Here, standing among the flowers, I would watch the shining little birds coming and going, each bird spending a minute or two sucking honey, then vanishing back into the shadowy trees, and from fifty to a hundred of them would always be in sight all around me at a time. Here all three species were feeding together; but I was familiar with the habits of only one, the bird I describe here.

The Glittering Humming-bird appears in the vicinity of Buenos Ayres in September, and later in the spring is found everywhere on the pampas where there are plantations, but it is never seen on the treeless plains. Its sudden appearance in considerable numbers in plantations on the pampas, where there are flowers to which it is partial, like those of the acacia tree, and its just as sudden departure when the flowers have fallen, have led me to conclude that its migration extends much further south, probably into mid-Patagonia. Like most Humming-birds it is an exquisitely beautiful little creature, in its glittering green mantle; and in its aerial life and swift motions a miracle of energy. To those who have seen the Humming-bird in a state of nature all descriptions of its appearance and movements must seem idle. In the life-habits of the *Trochilidæ* there is a singular monotony; and the Glittering Humming-bird differs little in its customs from other species that have been described. It is extremely pugnacious; the males meet to fight in the air, and rapidly ascend, revolving round each other, until when at a considerable height they suddenly separate and dart off in opposite directions. Occasionally two or three are seen flashing by, pursuing each other, with such velocity that even the Swift's flight, which is said to cover four hundred miles an hour, seems slow in comparison. This species also possesses the habit of darting towards a person and hovering bee-like for some time close to his face. It also flies frequently into a house, at window or door, but does not, like birds of other kinds, become confused on such occasions, and is much too lively to allow its retreat to be cut off. It feeds a great deal on minute spiders, and is fond of exploring the surfaces of mud and brick walls, where it is seen deftly inserting its slender crimson bill into the small spider-holes in search of prey. The nest, like that of most humming-birds, is a small, beautifully-made structure, composed of a variety of materials held closely together with spiders' webs, and is placed on a branch, or in a fork, or else suspended from slender drooping vines or twigs. Sometimes the nest is suspended to the thatch overhanging the eaves of a cottage, for except where persecuted the bird is quite fearless of man's presence. The eggs are two, and white.

Besides the little creaking chirp uttered at short intervals while flying or hovering, this species has a set song, composed of five or six tenuous and squeaking notes, uttered in rapid succession when the bird is perched. It is a song like that of the European Goldcrest *in shape*, and resembles it in sound, but is less musical, or more squeaky.

GUIRA CUCKOO

Guira piririgua

Above dark brown with white shaft-stripes; head brown; wings reddish brown; rump white; tail white, crossed by a broad black band, the two central feathers uniform brown; beneath dull white; throat and breast with long linear black shaft-stripes; bill and feet yellow; length 15 inches. Female similar.

PIRIRIGUA, the specific term adopted by naturalists for this bird, is, according to Azara, the vernacular name of the species in Paraguay. He says in that country it is abundant, but scarce in the Plata district. No doubt it has greatly increased and extended its range southwards during the hundred years which have elapsed since his time, as it is now very common in Buenos Ayres, where its vernacular name is *Urraca* (Magpie). In the last-named country it is not yet quite in harmony with its environment. Everywhere its habit is to feed exclusively on the ground, in spite of possessing feet formed for climbing; but its very scanty plumage, slow laborious flight, and long square tail, so unsuitable in cold boisterous weather, show that the species is a still unmodified intruder from the region of perpetual summer many degrees nearer to the equator.

The Guira Cuckoo is about sixteen inches long, has red eyes and blue feet, and an orange-red beak. The crown of the head is deep rufous, and the loose hair-like feathers are lengthened into a pointed crest. The back and rump are white, the wings and other upper parts very deep fuscous, marked with white and pale brown. Under surface dull white, with hair-like black marks on the throat and breast. The tail is square, nine to ten inches long; the two middle feathers dark brown, the others three-coloured—

yellow at the base, the middle portion dark glossy green, the ends white; and when the bird is flying the tail, spread out like a fan, forms a conspicuous and beautiful object.

During the inclement winter of Buenos Ayres the Guira Cuckoo is a miserable bird, and appears to suffer more than any other creature from cold. In the evening the flock, usually composed of from a dozen to twenty individuals, gathers on the thick horizontal branch of a tree sheltered from the wind, the birds crowding close together for warmth, and some of them roosting perched on the backs of their fellows. I have frequently seen them roosting three deep, one or two birds at the top to crown the pyramid; but with all their huddling together a severe frost is sure to prove fatal to one or more birds in the flock; and sometimes several birds that have dropped from the branch stiff with cold are found under the trees in the morning. If the morning is fair the flock betakes itself to some large tree, on which the sun shines, to settle on the outermost twigs on the northern side, each bird with its wings drooping, and its back turned towards the sun. In this spiritless attitude they spend an hour or two warming their blood and drying the dew from their scanty dress. During the day they bask much in the sun, and towards evening may be again seen on the sunny side of a hedge or tree warming their backs in the last rays. It is owing, no doubt, to its fecundity and to an abundance of food that the Guira Cuckoo is able to maintain its existence so far south in spite of its terrible enemy the cold.

With the return of warm weather this species becomes active, noisy, and the gayest of birds; the flock constantly wanders about from place to place, the birds flying in a scattered desultory manner one behind the other, and incessantly uttering while on the wing a long complaining cry. At intervals during the day they also utter a kind of song, composed of a series of long modulated whistling notes, two-syllabled, the first powerful and vehement, and becoming at each repetition lower and shorter, then ending in a succession of hoarse internal sounds like the stertorous breathing of a sleeping man. When approached all the birds break out into a chorus of alarm, with rattling notes so annoyingly loud and sustained that the intruder, be it man or beast, is generally glad to hurry out of ear-shot. As the breeding-season approaches they are heard, probably the males, to utter a variety of soft low chattering notes, sounding sometimes like a person laughing and crying together : the flock then breaks up into pairs, the birds becoming silent and very circumspect in their movements. The nest is usually built in a thorn-tree, of rather large sticks, a rough large structure, the inside often lined with green leaves plucked from the trees. The eggs are large for the bird, and usually six or seven in number ; but the number varies greatly, and I have known one bird lay as many as fourteen. They are elliptical in form and beautiful beyond comparison, being of an exquisite turquoise-blue, the whole shell roughly spattered with white. The white spots are composed of a soft calcareous substance, apparently deposited on the surface of the shell after its complete formation : they are raised, and look like snow-flakes, and when the egg is fresh-laid may be easily washed off with cold water, and are so extremely delicate that their purity is lost on the egg being taken into the hand. The young birds hatched from these lovely eggs are proverbial for their ugliness, *Pichon de Urraca* being a term of contempt commonly applied

to a person remarkable for want of comeliness. They
are as unclean as they are ugly, so that the nest,
usually containing six or seven young, is unpleasant
both to sight and smell. There is something
ludicrous in the notes of these young birds, resembling as they do the shrill half-hysterical laughter
of a female exhausted by over-indulgence in mirth.
One summer there was a large brood in a tree close
to my home, and every time we heard the parent
bird hastening to her nest with food in her beak,
and uttering her plaintive cries, we used to run to
the door to hear them. As soon as the old bird
reached the nest they would burst forth into such
wild extravagant peals and continue them so long
that we could not but think it a rare amusement to
listen to them.

According to Azara the Guira Cuckoo in Paraguay
has very friendly relations with the Ani (*Crotophaga
ani*), the birds consorting together in one flock, and
even laying their eggs in one nest; and he affirms
that he has seen nests containing eggs of both species.
These nests were probably brought to him by his
Indian collectors, who were in the habit of deceiving
him, and it is more than probable that in this matter
they were practising on his credulity; though it is
certain that birds of different species do sometimes
lay in one nest, as I have found—the Common Teal
and the Tinamu for instance. I also doubt very
much that the bird is ever polygamous, as Azara
suspected; but it frequently wastes eggs, and its
procreant habits are sometimes very irregular and
confusing, as the following case will show:

A flock numbering about sixteen individuals
passed the winter in the trees about my home, and
in spring scattered about the plantation, screaming
and chattering in their usual manner when about

to breed. I watched them, and found that after a time the flock broke up into small parties of three or four, and not into couples, and I could not detect them building. At length I discovered three broken eggs on the ground, and on examining the tree overhead found an incipient nest composed of about a dozen sticks laid crossways and out of which the eggs had been dropped. This was in October, and for a long time no other attempt at a nest was made ; but wasted eggs were dropped in abundance on the ground, and I continued finding them for about four months. Early in January another incipient nest was found, and on the ground beneath it six broken eggs. At the end of that month two large nests were made, each nest by one pair of birds, and in the two fourteen or fifteen young birds were reared.

When taken young the Guira Cuckoos become very tame, and make bold, noisy, mischievous pets, fond of climbing over and tugging at the clothes, buttons, and hair of their master or mistress. They appear to be more intelligent than most birds, and in a domestic state resemble the Magpie. I knew one tame Cuckoo that would carry off and jealously conceal bits of bright-coloured ribbon, thread, or cloth. In a wild state their food consists largely of insects, which they sometimes pursue running and flying along the ground. They also prey on mice and small reptiles, and carry off the fledglings from the nests of Sparrows and other small birds, and in spring they are frequently seen following the plough to pick up worms.

PATAGONIAN PARROT

Conurus patagonus

Above dark olive-green ; wings edged with bluish ; lower part of
back yellow ; beneath olive-green, darkest on throat ; whitish band
across the neck ; belly yellow, with patch in the middle and thighs
dark crimson ; length 18, wing 9.2, tail 10.5 inches. Female similar.

THIS Parrot, called in La Plata the Bank- or Bur-
rowing-Parrot, from its nesting-habits, is the only
member of its order found so far south as Patagonia.
In habits it differs somewhat from most of its congeners, and it may be regarded, I think, as one of
those species which are dying out—possibly owing
to the altered conditions resulting from the settlement of the country by Europeans. It was formerly
abundant on the southern pampas of La Plata, and
being partially migratory its flocks ranged in winter
to Buenos Ayres, and even as far north as the Paraná
river. When, as a child, I lived near the capital city
(Buenos Ayres), I remember that I always looked
forward with the greatest delight to the appearance
of these noisy dark-green winter visitors. Now they
are rarely seen within a hundred miles of Buenos
Ayres ; and I have been informed by old gauchos
that half a century before my time they invariably
appeared in immense flocks in winter, and have since
gradually diminished in numbers, until now in that
district the Bank-Parrot is almost a thing of the past.
Two or three hundreds of miles south of Buenos
Ayres city they are still to be met with in rather
large flocks, and have a few ancient breeding-places,
to which they cling very tenaciously. Where there
are trees or bushes on their feeding-ground they
perch on them ; they also gather the berries of the
Empetrum rubrum and other fruits from the bushes ;
but they feed principally on the ground, and while

the flock feeds one bird is invariably perched on a stalk or other elevation to act as sentinel. They are partial to the seeds of the giant thistle (*Carduus mariana*) and the wild pumpkin, and to get at the latter they bite the hard dry shell into pieces with their powerful beaks. When a horseman appears in the distance they rise in a compact flock, with loud harsh screams, and hover above him, within a very few yards of his head, their combined dissonant voices producing an uproar which is only equalled in that pandemonium of noises, the Parrot-house in the Zoological Gardens of London. They are extremely social, so much so that their flocks do not break up in the breeding-season; and their burrows, which they excavate in a perpendicular cliff or high bank, are placed close together; so that when the gauchos take the young birds—esteemed a great delicacy—the person who ventures down by means of a rope attached to his waist is able to rifle a colony. The burrow is three to five feet deep, and four white eggs are deposited on a slight nest at the extremity. I have only tasted the old birds, and found their flesh very bitter, scarcely palatable.

The natives say that this species cannot be taught to speak; and it is certain that the few individuals I have seen tame were unable to articulate.

Doubtless these Parrots were originally stray colonists from the tropics, although now resident in so cold a country as Patagonia. When viewed closely one would also imagine that they must at one time have been brilliant-plumaged birds; but either natural selection or the direct effect of a bleak climate has given a sombre shade to their colours—green, blue, yellow, and crimson; and when seen flying at a distance, or in cloudy weather, they look as dark as crows.

GREEN PARRAKEET

Bolborhynchus monachus

Green; front grey; wings blackish with slight bluish edgings;
beneath grey; bill whitish; length 11 inches. Female similar.

THE Common Green Parrakeet, called *Cotorra* or
Catita in the vernacular, is a well-known resident
species in the Argentine Republic. It is a lively,
restless bird, shrill-voiced, and exceedingly voci-
ferous, living and breeding in large communities,
and though it cannot learn to speak so distinctly
as some of the larger Parrots, it is impossible to
observe its habits without being convinced that it
shares in the intelligence of the highly-favoured order
to which it belongs.

In Buenos Ayres it was formerly very much more
numerous than it is now; but it is exceedingly
tenacious of its breeding-places, and there are some
few favoured localities where it still exists in large
colonies, in spite of the cruel persecution all birds
easily killed are subjected to in a country where
laws relating to such matters are little regarded,
and where the agricultural population is chiefly
Italian. At Mr. Gibson's residence near Cape San
Antonio, on the Atlantic coast, there is still a large
colony of these birds inhabiting the Tala woods
(*Celtis tala*), and I take the following facts from one
of his papers, contributed many years ago to the *Ibis*,
on the ornithology of the district.

He describes the woods as being full of their nests,
with their bright-coloured talkative denizens, and
their noisy chatter all day long drowning every other
sound. They are extremely sociable and breed in
communities. When a person enters the wood, their
subdued chatter suddenly ceases, and during the

ominous silence a hundred pairs of black beady eyes survey the intruder from the nests and branches; and then follow a whirring of wings and an outburst of screams that spread the alarm throughout the woods. The nests are frequented all the year, and it is rare to find a large one unattended by some of the birds any time during the day. In summer and autumn they feed principally on the thistle; first the flower is cut up and pulled to pieces for the sake of the green kernel, and later they eat the fallen seed on the ground. Their flight is rapid, with quick flutters of the wings, which seem never to be raised to the level of the body. They pay no regard to a *Polyborus* or *Milvago* (the Carrion Eagle and Carrion Hawk), but mob any other bird of prey appearing in the woods, all the Parrakeets rising in a crowd and hovering about it with angry screams.

The nests are suspended from the extremities of the branches, to which they are firmly woven. New nests consist of only two chambers, the porch and the nest proper, and are inhabited by a single pair of birds. Successive nests are added, until some of them come to weigh a quarter of a ton, and contain material enough to fill a large cart. Thorny twigs, firmly interwoven, form the only material, and there is no lining in the breeding-chamber, even in the breeding-season. Some old forest trees have seven or eight of these huge structures suspended from the branches, while the ground underneath is covered with twigs and remains of fallen nests. The entrance to the chamber is generally underneath, or if at the side is protected by an overhanging eave to prevent the intrusion of opossums. These entrances lead into the porch or outer chamber, and the latter communicates with the breeding-chamber. The breeding-chambers are not connected with each other, and each set is used by one pair of birds.

The number of pairs does not exceed a dozen,
even with the largest nests. Repairs are carried on
all the year round, but new nests are only added at
the approach of spring. Opossums are frequently
found in one of the higher chambers, when the
entrance has been made too high, but though they
take up their abode there they cannot reach the
other chambers, and the Parrakeets refuse to go away.
A species of Teal (probably *Querquedula brasiliensis*)
also sometimes occupies and breeds in their chambers, and in one case Mr. Gibson found an opossum
domiciled in an upper chamber, Parrakeets occupying
all the others except one, in which a Teal was sitting
on eggs.

The breeding-season begins about 1st November,
and as many as seven or eight eggs are laid ; these
are dull white, very thin-shelled, elongated, and have
the greatest diameter exactly equidistant from the
two ends.

Mr. Barrows speaks as follows of this species in
Entrerios : " An abundant and familiar bird in
the neighbourhood of Concepcion through the entire
year. It is commonly seen in flocks of twenty and
upwards, visiting grain-fields, gardens, etc., and
sometimes, if I was correctly informed, completely
stripping the grain-fields. They nest in communities,
many pairs uniting in the building of a large common
nest or mass of nests. I only saw these nests on two
occasions, and had no opportunity of examining
their structure. They were placed on high trees,
and appeared from below to be simply irregular
masses, six or eight feet in diameter, formed of
small sticks and twigs. Where the nests are abundant the natives destroy the young by hundreds,
and the ' squabs ' when nearly grown are said to
be very fine eating. The young are easily tamed,
and may be taught to articulate a few simple words."

BURROWING-OWL

Speotyto cunicularia

Above dark sandy brown, with large white oval spots and small
spots and freckles of pale brown; wings with broad whitish cross-
bars; facial disk greyish brown; beneath white; length 10, wing 7.5,
tail 3.5 inches. Female similar, but larger.

THE Burrowing-Owl is abundant everywhere on the
pampas of Buenos Ayres and avoids woods, but not
districts abounding in scattered trees and bushes.
It sees much better than most Owls by day, and
never affects concealment nor appears confused by
diurnal sounds and the glare of noon. It stares
fixedly—" with insolence," Azara says—at a passer-
by, following him with the eyes, the round head
turning about as on a pivot. If closely approached
it drops its body or bobs in a curious fashion, emitting a brief scream, followed by three abrupt ejacula-
tions; and if made to fly goes only fifteen or twenty
yards away, and alights again with face towards the
intruder; and no sooner does it alight than it repeats
the odd gesture and scream, standing stiff and erect,
and appearing beyond measure astonished at the
intrusion. By day it flies near the surface with wings
continuously flapping, and invariably before alighting
glides upwards for some distance and comes down
very abruptly. It frequently runs rapidly on the
ground, and is incapable of sustaining flight long.
Gaucho boys pursue these birds for sport on horseback, taking them after a chase of fifteen or twenty
minutes. As a boy I have myself taken many. They
live in pairs all the year, and sit by day at the mouth
of their burrow or on the Vizcacha's mound, the
two birds so close together as to be almost touching;
when alarmed they both fly away, but sometimes

the male only, the female diving into the burrow. On the pampas it may be more from necessity than choice that they always sit on the ground, as they are usually seen perched on the summits of bushes where such abound, as in Patagonia.

These are the commonest traits of the Burrowing-Owl in the settled districts, where it is excessively numerous and has become familiar with man ; but in the regions hunted over by the Indians it is a scarce bird and has different habits. Shy of approach as a persecuted game-fowl, it rises to a considerable height in the air when the approaching traveller is yet far off, and flies often beyond sight before descending again to the earth. This wildness of disposition is, without doubt, due to the active animosity of the pampas tribes, who have all the ancient widespread superstitions regarding the Owl. "Sister of the Evil Spirit" is one of their names for it ; they hunt it to death whenever they can, and when travelling will not stop to rest or encamp on a spot where an Owl has been spied. Where the country is settled by Europeans the bird has dropped its wary habits and become extremely tame. They are tenacious of the spot they live in, and are not easily driven out by cultivation. When the fields are ploughed up they make their kennels on their borders, or at the roadsides, and sit all day perched on the posts of the fences.

Occasionally they are seen preying by day, especially when anything passes near them, offering the chance of an easy capture. I have often amused myself by throwing bits of hard clay near one as it sat beside its kennel ; for the bird will immediately give chase, only discovering its mistake when the object is firmly clutched in its talons. When there are young to be fed, they are almost as active by day as by night. On hot November days multitudes of a large species of *Scarabæus* appear, and the bulky bodies and noisy bungling flight of these beetles invite the Owls to pursuit, and on every side they are seen pursuing and striking down the beetles, and tumbling upon them in the grass. Owls have a peculiar manner of taking their prey ; they grapple it so tightly in their talons that they totter and strive to steady themselves by throwing out their wings, and sometimes, losing their balance, fall prostrate and flutter on the ground. If the animal captured be small they proceed after a while to despatch it with the beak ; if large they usually rise laboriously from the ground and fly to some distance with it, thus giving time for the wounds inflicted by the claws to do their work.

At sunset the Owls begin to hoot ; a short followed by a long note is repeated many times with an interval of a second of silence. There is nothing dreary or solemn in this performance ; the voice is rather soft and sorrowful, somewhat resembling the lowest notes of the flute in sound. In spring they hoot a great deal, many individuals responding to each other.

In the evening they are often seen hovering like a Kestrel at a height of forty feet above the surface, and continuing to do so fully a minute or longer without altering their position. They do not drop the whole distance at once on their prey, but descend vertically, tumbling and fluttering as if wounded, to within ten yards of the earth, and then, after hovering a few seconds more, glide obliquely on to it. They prey on every living creature not too large to be overcome by them. Sometimes when a mouse is caught they tear off the head, tail, and feet, devouring only the body. The hind quarters of toads and frogs are almost invariably rejected; and inasmuch as these are the most fleshy and succulent parts, this is a strange and unaccountable habit. They make an easy conquest of a snake eighteen inches long, and kill it by dealing it blows with the beak, hopping briskly about it all the time, apparently to guard themselves with their wings. They prey largely on the common *Coronella anomala*, but I have never seen one attacking a venomous species. When they have young many individuals become destructive to poultry, coming about the houses and carrying off the chickens and ducklings by day. In seasons of plenty they destroy far more prey than they can devour; but in severe winters they come, apparently starving, about the houses, and will then stoop to carry off any dead animal food, though old and dried up as a piece of parchment. This I have often seen them do.

Though the Owls are always on familiar terms with the Vizcachas (*Lagostomus trichodactylus*) and occasionally breed in one of their disused burrows, as a rule they excavate a breeding-place for themselves. The kennel they make is crooked, and varies in length from four to twelve feet. The nest is placed at the extremity, and is composed of wool or dry grass, often exclusively of dry horse-dung. The eggs are usually five in number, white, and nearly spherical; the number, however, varies, and I have frequently found six or seven eggs in a nest. After the female has begun laying the birds continue carrying in dry horse-dung, until the floor of the burrow and a space before it is thickly carpeted with this material. The following spring the loose earth and rubbish is cleared out, for the same hole may serve them two or three years. It is always untidy, but mostly so during the breeding-season, when prey is very abundant, the floor and ground about the entrance being often littered with castings, green beetle-shells, pellets of hair and bones, feathers of birds, hind quarters of frogs in all stages of decay, great hairy spiders (*Mygale*), remains of half-eaten snakes, and other unpleasant creatures that they subsist on. But all this carrion about the little Owl's disordered house reminds one forcibly of the important part the bird plays in the economy of nature. The young birds ascend to the entrance of the burrow to bask in the sun and receive the food their parents bring; when approached they become irritated, snapping with their beaks, and retreat reluctantly into the hole; and for some weeks after leaving it they make it a refuge from danger. Old and young birds sometimes live together for four or five months. I believe that nine-tenths of the Owls on the pampas make their own burrows, but as they occasionally take possession of the forsaken holes of mammals to breed in, it is probable that they would always observe this last habit if suitable holes abounded, as on the North American prairies inhabited by the marmot. Probably our Burrowing-Owl originally acquired the habit of breeding in the ground in the open level regions it frequented; and when this habit (favourable as it must have been in such unsheltered situations) had become ineradicable, a want of suitable burrows would lead it to clean out such old ones as had become choked up with rubbish, to deepen such as were too shallow, and ultimately to excavate for itself. The mining instinct varies greatly in strength, even on the pampas. Some pairs, long mated, only begin to dig when the breeding season is already on them; others make their burrows as early as April—that is, six months before the breeding-season. Generally both birds work, one standing by and regarding operations with an aspect of grave interest, and taking its place in the pit when the other retires ; but sometimes the female has no assistance from her partner, and the burrow then is very short. Some pairs work expeditiously and their kennel is deep and neatly made ; others go about their task in a perfunctory manner, and begin, only to abandon, perhaps half a dozen burrows, and then rest two or three weeks from their unprofitable labours. But whether industrious or indolent, by September they all have their burrows made. I can only account for Azara's unfortunate statement, repeated by scores of compilers, that the Owl never constructs its own habitations, by assuming that a century ago, when he lived and when the country was still very sparsely settled, this Owl had not yet become so abundant or laid aside the wary habit the aborigines had taught it, so that he did not become very familiar with its habits.

CROWNED EAGLE

Harpyhaliaëtus coronatus

Above ashy brown, with a long crest of darker feathers ; wings grey with blackish tips ; tail black with a broad white median band and white tip ; beneath pale ashy brown ; length 33, wing 22 inches. Female similar but larger.

I MET with this fine Eagle on the Rio Negro, in Patagonia, where d'Orbigny also found it ; the entire Argentine territory comes, however, within its range. Having merely seen it perched on the tall willows fringing the Rio Negro, or soaring in wide circles far up in the sky, I cannot venture to speak of its habits, while the account of them which d'Orbigny built up is not worth quoting, for he does not say how he got his information. One of his statements would, if true, be very important indeed. He says that his attention was drawn to a very curious fact concerning the Crowned Harpy, which was, that this bird preys chiefly on the skunk—an animal, he very truly adds, with so pestilential an odour that even the most carnivorous of mammals are put to flight by it ; that it is the only bird of prey that kills the skunk, and that it does so by precipitating itself from a vast height upon its quarry, which it then quickly despatches. It would not matter at all whether the Eagle dropped from a great or a moderate height, for in either case the skunk would receive its enemy with the usual pestilent discharge. D'Orbigny's account is, however, pure conjecture, and though he does not tell us what led him to form such a conclusion, I have no doubt that it was because the Eagle or Eagles he obtained had the skunk-smell

on their plumage. Most of the Eagles I shot in Patagonia, including about a dozen Chilian Eagles, smelt
of skunk, the smell being in most cases old and faint.
Of two Crowned Harpies obtained, only one smelt
of skunk. This only shows that in Patagonia Eagles
attack the skunk, which is not strange considering
that it is of a suitable size and conspicuously marked ;
that it goes about fearlessly in the daytime and is the
most abundant animal, the small cavy excepted, in
that sterile country. But whether the Eagles *succeed*
in their attacks on it is a very different matter. The
probability is that when an Eagle, incited by the
pangs of hunger, commits so great a mistake as to
attack a skunk, the pestilent fluid, which has the
same terribly burning and nauseating effects on the
lower animals as on man, very quickly makes it
abandon the contest. It is certain that pumas make
the same mistake as the Eagles do, for in some that
are caught the fur smells strongly of skunk. It might
be said that the fact that many Eagles smell of skunk
serves to show that they do feed on them, for otherwise they would learn by experience to avoid so dangerous an animal, and the smell of a first encounter
would soon wear off. I do not think that hungry
birds of prey, in a barren country like Patagonia,
would learn from one repulse, or even from several,
the fruitlessness and danger of such attacks ; while
the smell is so marvellously persistent that one or
two such attacks a year on the part of each Eagle
would be enough to account for the smell on so
many birds. If skunks could be easily conquered
by Eagles, they would not be so numerous or so
neglectful of their safety as we find them.

PEREGRINE FALCON

Falco peregrinus

Above plumbeous, lightest on the rump, more or less distinctly barred with black; head and cheeks black; beneath white tinged with cinnamon; abdomen and thighs traversed by narrow black bands; cere and feet yellow; length 20, wing 14 inches. Female similar; a third larger.

THE Peregrine Falcon is found throughout the Argentine Republic, but is nowhere numerous, and is not migratory; nor is it " essentially a duck-hawk," as in India according to Dr. Anderson, for it preys chiefly on land birds. It is solitary, and each bird possesses a favourite resting-place or *home*, where it spends several hours every day, and also roosts at night. Where there are trees it has its chosen site where it may always be found at noon; but on the open treeless pampas a mound of earth or the bleached skull of a horse or cow serves it for a perch, and here for months the bird may be found every day on its stand. It sits upright and motionless, springs suddenly into the air when taking flight, and flies in a straight line, and with a velocity which few birds can equal. Its appearance always causes great consternation amongst other birds, for even the Spur-winged Lapwing, the spirited persecutor of all other Hawks, flies screaming with terror from it. It prefers attacking moderately large birds, striking them on the wing, after which it stoops to pick them up. While out riding one day I saw a Peregrine sweep down from a great height and strike a Burrowing-Owl to the earth, the Owl having risen up before me. It then picked it up and flew away with it in its talons.

The Peregrine possesses one very curious habit. When a Plover, Pigeon, or Duck is killed, it eats the skin and flesh of the head and neck, picking the vertebræ clean of the flesh down to the breast-bone, and also eating the eyes, but leaving the body untouched. I have found scores of dead birds with head and neck picked clean in this way ; and once I watched for some months a Peregrine which had established itself near my home, where it made havoc among the Pigeons ; and I frequently marked the spot to which it carried its prey, and on going to the place always found that the Pigeon's head and neck only had been stripped of flesh. The Burrowing Owl has an analogous habit, for it invariably rejects the hind quarters of the toads and frogs which it captures.

At the approach of the warm season the Peregrines are often seen in twos and threes violently pursuing each other at a great height in the air, and uttering shrill, piercing screams, which can be heard distinctly after the birds have disappeared from sight.

PIGMY FALCON

Spiziapteryx circumcinctus

Above brown with black shaft-stripes; head black with brown stripes and white superciliaries which join round the nape; rump white; wings black with white oval spots on the outer and white bars on the inner webs; tail black, all but the central feathers crossed by five or six broad white bars; beneath white, the breast marked with narrow black shaft-stripes; beak plumbeous, lower mandible yellow; feet greenish; length 11, wing 6.5 inches. Female similar, rather larger.

THIS small Hawk is sometimes met with in the woods of La Plata, near the river; it is rare, but owing to its curious violent flight, with the short blunt wings rapidly beating all the time, it is very conspicuous in the air and well known to the natives, who call it *Rey de los Pájaros* (King of the Birds) and entertain a very high opinion of its energy and strength. I have never seen it taking its prey, and do not believe that it ever attempts to capture anything in the air, its short, blunt wings and peculiar manner of flight being unsuited for such a purpose. Probably it captures birds by a sudden dash when they mob it on its perch; and I do not know any Raptor more persistently run after and mobbed by small birds. I once watched one for upwards of an hour as it sat on a tree attended by a large flock of Guira Cuckoos, all excitedly screaming and bent on dislodging it from its position. So long as they kept away five or six feet from it the Hawk remained motionless, only hissing and snapping occasionally as a warning; but whenever a Cuckoo ventured a little nearer and into the charmed circle, it would make a sudden rapid dash and buffet the intruder violently back to a proper distance, returning afterwards to its own stand.

CHIMANGO, OR COMMON CARRION HAWK

Milvago chimango

Upper plumage reddish brown; greater wing-coverts white with slight brown cross-bars; tail greyish white, banded and freckled with greyish brown. Under plumage grey, tinged with rufous on throat and breast; length 15, wing 11, tail 6.5 inches. Sexes alike.

AZARA says of the Carancho (*Polyborus tharus*): " All methods of subsistence are known to this bird : it pries into, understands, and takes advantage of everything." These words apply better to the Chimango, which has probably the largest bill of fare of any bird, and has grafted on to its own peculiar manner of life the habits of twenty diverse species. By turns it is a Falcon, a Vulture, an insect-eater, and a vegetable-eater. On the same day you will see one bird in violent Hawk-like pursuit of its living prey, with all the instincts of rapine hot within it, and another less ambitious individual engaged in laboriously tearing at an old cast-off shoe, uttering mournful notes the while, but probably more concerned at the tenacity of the material than at its indigestibility.

A species so cosmopolitan in its tastes might have had a whole volume to itself in England ; being only a poor foreigner it has had no more than a few unfriendly paragraphs bestowed upon it. For it happens to be a member of that South-American sub-family of which even grave naturalists have spoken slightingly, calling them vile, cowardly, contemptible birds ; and the Chimango is nearly least of them all—a sort of poor relation and hanger-on of a family already looked upon as bankrupt and disreputable. Despite this evil reputation, few species are more deserving of careful study; for throughout an extensive portion of South America it is the commonest bird we know; and when we consider how closely connected are the lives of all living creatures by means of their interlacing relations, so that the predominance of any one kind, however innocuous, necessarily causes the modification, or extinction even, of surrounding species, we are better able to appreciate the importance of this despised fowl in the natural polity. Add to this its protean habits, and then, however poor a creature our bird may seem, and deserving of strange-sounding epithets from an ethical point of view, I do not know where the naturalist will find a more interesting one.

The Chimango has not an engaging appearance. In size and figure it much resembles the Hen-Harrier, and the plumage is uniformly of a light sandy brown colour; the shanks are slender, claws weak, and beak so slightly hooked that it seems like the merest apology of the Falcon's tearing weapon. It has an easy, loitering flight, and when on the wing does not appear to have an object in view, like the Hawk, but wanders and prowls about here and there, and when it spies another bird it flies after him to see if he has food in his eye. When one finds something to eat the others try to deprive him of it, pursuing him with great determination all over the place; if the foremost pursuer flags, a fresh bird takes its place, until the object of so much contention— perhaps after all only a bit of bone or skin—is dropped to the ground, to be instantly snatched up by some bird in the tail of the chase; and he in turn becomes the pursued of all the others. This continues until one grows tired and leaves off watching them without seeing the result. They are loquacious and sociable, frequently congregating in loose companies of thirty or forty individuals, when they spend several hours every day in spirited exercises, soaring about like Martins, performing endless evolutions, and joining in aerial mock battles. When tired of these pastimes they all settle down again, to remain for an hour or so perched on the topmost boughs of trees or on other elevations; and at intervals one bird utters a very long, leisurely chant, with a falling inflection, followed by a series of short notes, all the other birds joining in chorus and uttering short notes in time with those of their soloist or precentor. The nest is built on trees or rushes in swamps, or on the ground amongst grass and thistles. The eggs are three or four in number, nearly spherical, blotched with deep red on a white or creamy ground; sometimes the whole egg is marbled with red; but there are endless varieties. It is easy to find the nest, and becomes easier when there are young birds, for the parent when out foraging invariably returns to her young uttering long mournful notes, so that one has only to listen and mark the spot where it alights. After visiting a nest I have always found the young birds soon disappear, and as the old birds vanish also I believe that the Chimango removes its young when the nest has been discovered—a rare habit with birds.

Chimangos abound most in settled districts, but a prospect of food will quickly bring numbers together even in the most solitary places. On the desert pampas, where hunters, Indian and European, have a great fancy for burning the dead grass, the moment the smoke of a distant fire is seen there the Chimangos fly to follow the conflagration. They are at such times strangely animated, dashing through clouds of smoke, feasting among the hot ashes on roasted cavies and other small mammals, and boldly pursuing the scorched fugitives from the flames.

At all times and in all places the Chimango is ever ready to pounce on the weak, the sickly, and the wounded. In other regions of the globe these doomed ones fall into the clutches of the true bird of prey ; but the salutary office of executioner is so effectually performed by the Chimango and his congeners where these false Hawks abound, that the true Hawks have a much keener struggle to exist here. This circumstance has possibly served to make them swifter of wing, keener of sight, and bolder in attack than elsewhere. I have seen a Buzzard, which is not considered the bravest of the Hawks, turn quick as lightning on a Spur-wing Lapwing, which was pursuing it, and, grappling it, bear it down to the ground and despatch it in a moment, though a hundred other Lapwings were uttering piercing screams above it. Yet this Plover is a large, powerful, fierce-tempered bird, and armed with sharp spurs on its wings. This is but one of numberless instances I have witnessed of the extreme strength and daring of our Hawks.

When shooting birds to preserve I used to keep an anxious eye on the movements of the Chimangos flying about, for I have had some fine specimens carried off or mutilated by these omnipresent robbers. One winter day I came across a fine *Myiotheretes rufiventris*, a pretty and graceful Tyrant-bird, rather larger than the Common Thrush, with a chocolate and silver-grey plumage. It was rare in that place, and, anxious to secure it, I fired a very long shot, for it was extremely shy. It rose up high in the air and flew off apparently unconcerned. What then was my surprise to see a Chimango start off in pursuit of it! Springing on to my horse I followed, and before going half a mile noticed the Tyrant-bird beginning to show signs of distress. After avoiding several blows aimed by the Chimango, it flew down and plunged into a cardoon bush. There I captured it, and when skinning it to preserve found that one small shot had lodged in the fleshy portion of the breast. It was a very slight wound, yet the Chimango with its trained sight had noticed something wrong with the bird from the moment it flew off, apparently in its usual free, buoyant manner.

On another occasion I was defrauded of a more valuable specimen than the Tyrant-bird. It was on the east coast of Patagonia, when one morning, while seated on an elevation, watching the waves dashing themselves on the shore, I perceived a shining white object tossing about at some distance from land. Successive waves brought it nearer, till at last it was caught up and flung far out on to the shingle fifty yards from where I sat; and instantly, before the cloud of spray had vanished, a Chimango dashed down upon it. I jumped up and ran down as fast as I could, and found my white object to be a Penguin, apparently just killed by some accident out at sea, and in splendid plumage; but alas! in that moment the vile Chimango had stripped off and devoured the skin from its head, so that as a specimen it was hopelessly ruined.

As a rule, strong healthy birds despise the Chimango; they feed in his company; his sudden appearance causes no alarm, and they do not take the trouble to persecute him; but when they have eggs or young he is not to be trusted. He is not easily turned from a nest he has once discovered. I have seen him carry off a young Tyrant-bird (*Milvulus tyrannus*) in the face of such an attack from the parent birds that one would have imagined not even a true Hawk could have withstood. Curiously enough, like one of the boldest of our small Hawks (*Tinnunculus cinnamominus*), they sometimes attack birds so much too strong and big for them that they must know the assault will produce more annoyance than harm. I was once watching a flock of Coots feeding on a grassy bank, when a passing Chimango paused in its flight, and, after hovering over them a few moments, dashed down upon them with such impetuosity that several birds were thrown to the ground by the quick successive blows of its wings. There they lay on their backs, kicking, apparently too much terrified to get up, while the Chimango deliberately eyed them for some moments, then quietly flew away, leaving them to dash into the water and cool their fright. Attacks like these are possibly made in a sportive spirit, for the Milvago is a playful bird, and, as with many other species, bird and mammal, its play always takes the form of attack.

Its inefficient weapons compel it to be more timid than the Hawk, but there are many exceptions, and in every locality individual birds are found distinguished by their temerity. Almost any shepherd can say that his flock is subject to the persecutions of at least one pair of lamb-killing birds of this species. They prowl about the flock, and watch till a small lamb is found sleeping at some distance from its dam, rush upon it, and, clinging to its head, eat away its nose and tongue. The shepherd is then obliged to kill the lamb; but I have seen many lambs that have been permitted to survive the mutilation, and which have grown to strong healthy sheep, though with greatly disfigured faces. One more instance I will give of the boldness of a bird of which Azara, greatly mistaken, says that it might possibly have courage enough to attack a mouse, though he doubts it. Close to my house, when I was a boy, a pair of these birds had their nest near a narrow path leading through a thicket of giant thistles, and every time I traversed this path the male bird, which, contrary to the rule with birds of prey, is larger and bolder than the female, would rise high above me, then dashing down strike my horse a violent blow on the forehead with its wings. This action it would repeat till I was out of the path. I thought it very strange the bird never struck *my* head; but I presently discovered that it had an excellent reason for what it did. The gauchos ride by preference on horses never properly tamed, and one neighbour informed me that he was obliged every day to make a circuit of half a mile round the thistles, as the horses he rode became quite unmanageable in the path, they had been so terrified with the attacks of this Chimango.

Where the intelligence of the bird appears to be really at fault is in its habit of attacking a sore-backed horse, tempted thereto by the sight of a raw spot, and apparently not understanding that the flesh it wishes to devour is an inseparable part of the whole animal. Darwin has noticed this curious blunder of the bird; and I have often seen a chafed saddle-horse wildly scouring the plain closely pursued by a hungry Chimango, determined to dine on a portion of him.

In the hot season, when marshes and lagoons are drying up, the Chimango is seen associating with Ibises and other waders, standing knee-deep in the water and watching for tadpoles, frogs, and other aquatic prey. He also wades after a very different kind of food. At the bottom of pools, collected on clayey soil after a summer shower, an edible fungus grows, of a dull greenish colour and resembling gelatine. He has found out that this fungus is good for food, though I never saw any other creature eating it. In cultivated districts he follows the plough in company with the Black-headed Gulls, *Molothri,* Guira Cuckoos, and Tyrant-birds, and clumsily gleans amongst the fresh-turned mould for worms and larvæ. He also attends the pigs when they are rooting on the plain to share any succulent treasure turned up by their snouts ; for he is not a bird that allows dignity to stand between him and his dinner. In the autumn, on damp, sultry days, the red ants, that make small conical mounds on the pampas, are everywhere seen swarming. Rising high in the air they form a little cloud or column, and hang suspended for hours over the same spot. On such days the Milvagos fare sumptuously on little insects, and under each cloud of winged ants several of them are to be seen in company with a few Flycatchers, or other diminutive species, briskly running about to pick up the falling manna, their enjoyment undisturbed by any sense of incongruity.

Before everything, however, the Chimango is a vulture, and is to be found at every solitary rancho sharing with dogs and poultry the offal and waste meat thrown out on the dust-heap ; or, after the flock has gone to pasture, tearing at the eyes and tongue of a dead lamb in the sheepfold. When the hide has been stripped from a dead horse or cow on the plains, the Chimango is always first on the scene. While feeding on a carcase it incessantly utters a soliloquy of the most lamentable notes, as if protesting against the hard necessity of having to put up with such carrion fare—long querulous cries resembling the piteous whines of a shivering puppy

chained up in a bleak backyard and all its wants
neglected, but infinitely more doleful in character.
The gauchos have a saying comparing a man who
grumbles at good fortune to the Chimango crying
on a carcase — an extremely expressive saying to
those who have listened to the distressful wailings
of the bird over its meat. In winter a carcase attracts
a great concourse of the Black-backed Gulls ; for
with the cold weather these Vultures of the sea
abandon their breeding-places on the Atlantic shores
to wander in search of food over the vast inland
pampas. The dead beast is quickly surrounded by a
host of them, and the poor Chimango crowded out.
One at least, however, is usually to be seen perched
on the carcase tearing at the flesh, and at intervals
with outstretched neck and ruffled-up plumage
uttering a succession of its strange wailing cries,
reminding one of a public orator mounted on a
rostrum and addressing harrowing appeals to a
crowd of attentive listeners. When the carcase has
been finally abandoned by foxes, armadillos, Gulls,
and Caranchos, the Chimango still clings sorrow-
fully to it, eking out a miserable existence by tearing at a fringe of gristle and whetting his hungry
beak on the bones.

Though an inordinate lover of carrion, a wise
instinct has taught it that this aliment is unsuited to
the tender stomachs of its fledglings ; these it feeds
almost exclusively on the young of small birds. In
November the Chimangos are seen incessantly beating over the cardoon bushes, after the manner of
Hen-Harriers ; for at this season in the cardoons
breeds the *Synallaxis hudsoni*. This bird, sometimes
called *Téru-réru del campo* by the natives, is excessively shy and mouse-like in habits, seldom showing
itself, and by means of strong legs and a long, slender,
wedge-like body is able to glide swiftly as a snake

through and under the grass. In summer one hears its long, melancholy, trilling call-note from a cardoon bush, but if approached it drops to the ground and vanishes. Under the densest part of the cardoon bush it scoops out a little circular hollow in the soil, and constructs over it a dome of woven grass and thorns, leaving only a very small aperture ; it lines the floor with dry horse-dung, and lays five buff-coloured eggs. So admirably is the nest concealed that I have searched every day for it through a whole breeding-season without being rewarded with a single find. Yet they are easily found by the Chimango. In the course of a single day I have examined five or six broods of young Chimangos, and by pressing a finger on their distended crops made them disgorge their food, and found in every instance that they had been fed on nothing but the young of the Téru-réru. I was simply amazed at this whole-sale destruction of the young of a species so secret in its nesting-habits ; for no eye, even of a Hawk, can pierce through the leafage of a cardoon bush, ending near the surface in an accumulated mass of the dead and decaying portions of the plant. The explanation of the Chimango's success is to be found in the loquacious habit of the fledglings it preys on, a habit common in the young of Dendrocolaptine species. The intervals between the visits of the parent birds with food they spend in conversing together in their high-pitched tones. If a person approaches the solid fabric of the Oven-bird (*Furnarius rufus*) when there are young in it, he will hear shrill laughter-like notes and little choruses, like those uttered by the old birds, only feebler ; but in the case of that species no harm can result from the loquacity of the young, since the castle they inhabit is impregnable. Hovering over the cardoons, the Chimango listens for the stridulous laughter of the fledglings, and when he hears it the thorny covering is quickly pierced and the dome broken into.

Facts like these bring before us with startling vividness the struggle for existence, showing what great issues in the life of a species may depend on matters so trivial, seemingly, that to the uninformed mind they appear like the merest dust in the balance, which is not regarded. And how tremendous and pitiless is that searching law of the survival of the fittest in its operations, when we see a species like this *Synallaxis*, in the fashioning and perfecting of which Nature seems to have exhausted all her art, so exquisitely is it adapted in its structure, coloration, and habits to the one great object of concealment, yet apparently doomed to destruction through this one petty oversight—the irrepressible garrulity of the fledglings in their nest! It is, however, no oversight at all; since the law of natural selection is not prophetic in its action, and only preserves such variations as are beneficial in existing circumstances, without anticipating changes in the conditions. The settlement of the country has, no doubt, caused a great increase of Chimangos, and in some indirect way probably has served to quicken their intelligence; thus a change in the conditions which have moulded this *Synallaxis* brings a danger to it from an unexpected quarter. The situation of the nest exposes it, one would imagine, to attacks from snakes and small mammals, from bird-killing spiders, beetles and crickets, yet these subtle ground foes have missed it, while the baby-laughter of the little ones in their cradle has called down an unlooked-for destroyer from above. It might be answered that this must be a very numerous species, otherwise the Chimango could not have acquired the habit of finding the nests; that when they become rarer the pursuit will be given over, after which the balance will readjust itself. But in numbers there is safety, especially for a feeble, hunted species, unable from its peculiar structure to vary its manner of life. To such the remark made by Darwin, that "rarity is the precursor to extinction," applies with peculiar force.

CARANCHO CARRION-HAWK
Polyborus tharus (Mol.)

CARANCHO OR CARACÁRA

Polyborus tharus

Dark brown with whitish mottlings; head black; wings and tail greyish white with greyish brown cross-bars and black tips; beneath dark brown; throat and sides of head yellowish white; beak yellow; cere orange. Sexes alike.

THIS bird, which combines the raptorial instincts of the Eagle with the base carrion-feeding habits of the Vulture, has already had so many biographers that it might seem superfluous to speak of it again at any great length; only it happens to be one of those very versatile species about which there is always something fresh to be said; and, besides, I do not altogether agree with the very ignoble character usually ascribed to it by travellers. It is, however, probable that it varies greatly in disposition and habits in different districts. In Patagonia I was surprised at its dejected appearance and skulking cowardly manner, so unlike the bird I had been accustomed to see on the pampas. I shot several, and they were all in a miserably poor condition and apparently half-starved. It struck me that in that cold, sterile country, where prey is scarce, the Carancho is altogether out of place; for it there has to compete with Eagles and Vultures in large numbers; and these, it is almost needless to say, are, in their separate lines, stronger than the composite and less specialised Carancho. In Patagonia he is truly a "miserable bird," with a very frail hold on existence. How different on that illimitable grassy ocean farther north, where he is the lord of the feathered race, for Eagles and Vultures, that require mountains and trees to breed and roost on, do not come there

to set him aside ; there the conditions are suited to
him and have served to develop in him a wonderfully
bold and savage spirit.   When seen perched on a
conical ant-hill, standing erect above the tall plumy
grass, he has a fine, even a noble appearance ; but
when flying he is not handsome, the wings being
very bluntly rounded at the extremities and the
flight low and ungraceful.   The plumage is blackish
in the adult, brown in the young.   The sides of the
head and breast are creamy white, the latter transversely marked with black spots.   The crown is
adorned with a crest or top-knot.   The beak is much
larger than in Eagles and Vultures, and of a dull
blue colour ; the cere and legs are bright yellow.

The species ranges throughout South America,
and from Paraguay northwards is called everywhere, I believe, *Caracara*.   South of Paraguay the
Spanish name is *Carancho*, possibly a corruption of
Keanché, the Puelche name for the allied *Milvago
chimango*, in imitation of its peevish cry.   The
Indian name for the Carancho in these regions
is *Trarú* (from its harsh cry), misspelt *Tharú* by
Molina, a Spanish priest who wrote a book on the
birds of Chili in the eighteenth century ; hence the
specific name *tharus*.

The Caranchos pair for life, and may therefore be
called social birds ; they also often live and hunt in
families of the parent and young birds until the
following spring ; and at all times several individuals
will readily combine to attack their prey, but they
never live or move about in flocks.   Each couple
has its own home or resting-place, which they will
continue to use for an indefinite time, roosting on
the same branch and occupying the same nest year
after year ; while at all times the two birds are seen
constantly together and seem very much attached.

Azara relates that he once saw a male pounce down
on a frog, and carrying it to a tree call his mate to
him and make her a present of it. It was not a very
magnificent present, but the action seems to show
that the bird possesses some commendable qualities
which are seldom seen in the raptorial family.

In uninhabited places I have always found the
Caranchos just as abundant as in the settled districts;
and after a deer has been pulled down by the dogs
I have seen as many as seventy or eighty birds
congregate to feed on its flesh within half an hour,
although not one had been previously visible.
D'Orbigny describes the bird as a parasite on man,
savage and civilised, following him everywhere to
feed on the leavings when he slays wild or domestic
animals, and as being scarcely able to exist without
him. No doubt the bird does follow man greatly
to its advantage, but this is only in very thinly
settled and purely pastoral and hunting districts,
where a large proportion of the flesh of every animal
slain is given to the fowls of the air. Where the
population increases the Carancho quickly meets
with the fate of all large species which are regarded
as prejudicial.

Without doubt it is a carrion-eater, but only, I
believe, when it cannot get fresh provisions; for
when famished it will eat anything rather than study
its dignity and suffer hunger like the nobler Eagle.
I have frequently seen one or two or three of them
together on the ground under a column of winged
ants, eagerly feasting on the falling insects. To
eat putrid meat it must be very hungry indeed; it
is, however, amazingly fond of freshly-killed flesh,
and when a cow is slaughtered at an estancia-house
the Carancho quickly appears on the scene to claim
his share, and catching up the first thing he can

lift he carries it off before the dogs can deprive him of it. When he has risen to a height of five or six yards in the air he drops the meat from his beak and dexterously catches it in his claws without pausing or swerving in his flight. It is singular that the bird seems quite incapable of lifting anything from the ground with the claws, the beak being invariably used, even when the prey is an animal which it might seem dangerous to lift in this way. I once saw one of these birds swoop down on a rat from a distance of about forty feet, and rise with its struggling and squealing prey to a height of twenty feet, then drop it from his beak and gracefully catch it in his talons. Yet when it pursues and overtakes a bird in the air it invariably uses the claws in the same way as other Hawks. This I have frequently observed, and I give the two following anecdotes to show that even birds which one would imagine to be quite safe from the Carancho are on some occasions attacked by it.

While walking in a fallow field near my home one day I came on a Pigeon feeding, and at once recognised it as one which had only begun to fly about a week before ; for although a large number of Pigeons were kept, this bird happened to be of the purest unspotted white, and for a long time I had been endeavouring to preserve and increase the pure white individuals, but with very little success, for the Peregrines invariably singled them out for attack. A Carancho was circling about at some distance overhead, and while I stood still to watch and admire my Pigeon it stooped to within twenty yards of the surface and remained hovering over my head. Presently the Pigeon became alarmed and flew away, whereupon the Hawk gave chase—a very vain chase I imagined it would prove. It lasted for about half a minute, the Pigeon rushing wildly round in wide circles, now mounting aloft and now plunging downwards close to the surface, the Carancho hotly following all the time. At length, evidently in great terror, the hunted bird flew down, alighting within a yard of my feet. I stooped to take hold of it, when, becoming frightened at my action, it flew straight up and was seized in the talons of its pursuer close to my face and carried away.

In the next case the bird attacked was the Spur-winged Lapwing, the irreconcilable enemy of the Carancho and its bold and persistent persecutor. The very sight of this Hawk rouses the Lapwings to a frenzy of excitement, and springing aloft they hasten to meet it in mid-air, screaming loudly, and continue to harry it until it leaves their ground, after which they return, and, ranged in triplets, perform their triumphal dances, accompanied with loud drumming notes. But if their hated foe alights on the ground, or on some elevation near them, they hover about him, and first one, then another, rushes down with the greatest violence, and gliding near him turns the bend of its wings so that the spur appears almost to graze his head. While one bird is descending others are rising upwards to renew their charges ; and this persecution continues until they drive him away or become exhausted with their fruitless efforts. The Carancho, however, takes little notice of his tormentors ; only when the Plover comes very close, evidently bent on piercing his skull with its sharp weapon, he quickly dodges his head, after which he resumes his indifferent de-meanour until the rush of the succeeding bird takes place.

While out riding one day a Carancho flew past me attended by about thirty Lapwings, combined to hunt him from their ground, for it was near the breeding-season, when their jealous irascible temper is most excited. All at once, just as a Lapwing swept close by and then passed on before it, the Hawk quickened its flight in the most wonderful manner and was seen in hot pursuit of its tormentor. The angry hectoring cries of the Lapwings instantly changed to piercing screams of terror, which in a very short time brought a crowd numbering between two and three hundred birds to the rescue. Now, I thought, the hunted bird will escape, for it twisted and turned rapidly about, trying to lose itself amongst its fellows, all hovering in a compact crowd about it and screaming their loudest. But the Carancho was not to be shaken off; he was never more than a yard behind his quarry, and I was near enough to distinguish the piteous screams of the chased Lapwing amidst all the tumult, as of a bird already captive. At the end of about a minute it was seized in the Carancho's talons, and, still violently screaming, borne away. The cloud of Lapwings followed for some distance, but presently they all returned to the fatal spot where the contest had taken place; and for an hour afterwards they continued soaring about in separate bodies, screaming all the time with an unusual note in their voices as of fear or grief, and holding excited conclaves on the ground, to all appearance as greatly disturbed in their minds as an equal number of highly emotional human beings would be in the event of a similar disaster overtaking them.

It is not often, however, that the Carancho ventures singly to attack adult and vigorous birds, except the Tinamu, the " Partridge " of South America; they prey by preference on the young and ailing, on small lambs and pigs left at a distance by their dams ; and they also frequently attack and kill old and weakly sheep. Where anything is wrong with bird or beast they are very quick to detect it, and will follow a sportsman to pick up the wounded birds, intelligently keeping at a safe distance themselves. I once shot a Flamingo in the grey stage of plumage and had some trouble to cross the stream, on the opposite side of which the bird, wounded very slightly, was rapidly stalking away. In three or four minutes I was over and found my Flamingo endeavouring to defend itself against the assaults of a Carancho which had marked it for its own, and was striking it on the neck and breast in the most vigorous and determined way, sometimes from above, at other times alighting on the ground before it and springing up to strike like a game-cock. A spot of blood on the plumage of the wounded bird, which had only one wing slightly damaged, had been sufficient to call down the attack ; for to the Carancho a spot of blood, a drooping wing, or any irregularity in the gait, quickly tells its tale.

When several of these birds combine they are very bold. A friend told me that while voyaging on the Paraná river a Black-necked Swan flew past him hotly pursued by three Caranchos; and I also witnessed an attack by four birds on a widely different species. I was standing on the bank of a stream on the pampas watching a great concourse of birds of several kinds on the opposite shore, where the carcase of a horse, from which the hide had been stripped, lay at the edge of the water. One or two hundred Hooded Gulls and about a dozen Chimangos were gathered about the carcase, and close to them a very large flock of Glossy Ibises were wading about in the water, while amongst these, standing motionless in the water, was one solitary White Egret. Presently four Caranchos appeared, two adults and two young birds in brown plumage, and alighted on the ground near the carcase. The young birds advanced at once and began tearing at the flesh ; while the two old birds stayed where they had alighted, as if disinclined to feed on half-putrid meat. Presently one of them sprang into the air and made a dash at the birds in the water, and instantly all the birds in the place rose into the air screaming loudly, the two young brown Caranchos only remaining on the ground. For a few moments I was in ignorance of the meaning of all this turmoil, when, suddenly, out of the confused black and white cloud of birds the Egret appeared, mounting vertically upwards with vigorous measured strokes. A moment later, first one then the other Carancho also emerged from the cloud, evidently pursuing the Egret, and only then the two brown birds sprang into the air and joined in the chase. For some minutes I watched the four birds toiling upwards with a wild zig-zag flight, while the Egret, still rising vertically, seemed to leave them hopelessly far behind. But before long they reached and passed it, and each bird as he did so would turn and rush downwards, striking at the Egret with his claws, and while one descended the others were rising, bird following bird with the greatest regularity. In this way they continued toiling upwards until the Egret appeared a mere white speck in the sky, about which the four hateful black spots were still revolving. I had watched them from the first with the greatest excitement, and now began to fear that they would pass from sight and leave me in ignorance of the result ; but at length they began to descend, and then it looked as if the Egret had lost all hope, for it was dropping very rapidly, while the four birds were all close to it, striking at it every three or four seconds. The descent for the last half of the distance was exceedingly rapid, and the birds would have come down almost at the very spot they started from, which was about forty yards from where I stood, but the Egret was driven aside, and sloping rapidly down struck the earth at a distance of two hundred yards from the starting-point. Scarcely had it touched the ground before the hungry quartet were tearing it with their beaks. They were all equally hungry no doubt, and perhaps the old birds were even hungrier than their young; and I am quite sure that if the flesh of the dead horse had not been so far advanced towards putrefaction they would not have attempted the conquest of the Egret.

I have so frequently seen a pure white bird singled out for attack in this way, that it has always been a great subject of wonder to me how the two common species of snow-white Herons in South America are able to maintain their existence; for their whiteness exceeds that of other white waterfowl, while, compared with Swans, Storks, and the Wood-Ibis, they are small and feeble. I am sure that if these four Caranchos had attacked a Glossy Ibis they would have found it an easier conquest; yet they singled out the Egret, purely, I believe, on account of its shining white conspicuous plumage.

This wing-contest was a very splendid spectacle, and I was very glad that I had witnessed it, although it ended badly for the poor Egret; but in another case of a combined attack by Caranchos there was nothing to admire except the intelligence displayed by the birds in combining, and much to cause the mind to revolt against the blindly destructive ferocity exhibited by Nature in the instincts of her creatures. The scene was witnessed by a beloved old gaucho friend of mine, a good observer, who related it to me. It was in summer, and he was riding in a narrow bridle-path on a plain covered with a dense growth of giant thistles, nine or ten feet high, when he noticed some distance ahead several Caranchos hovering over the spot; and at once conjectured that some large animal had fallen there, or that a traveller had been thrown from his horse and was lying injured among the thistles. On reaching the spot he found an open space of ground about forty yards in diameter, surrounded by the dense wall of close-growing thistles, and over this place the birds were flying, while several others were stationed near, apparently waiting for something to happen. The attraction was a large male Rhea squatting on the ground, and sheltering with its extended wings a brood of young birds. My friend was not able to count them, but there were not fewer than twenty-five or thirty young birds, small tender things, only a day or so out of the shell. As soon as he rode into the open space of ground, the old Ostrich sprang up, and with lowered head, clattering beak, and broad wings spread out like sails, rushed at him; his horse was greatly terrified, and tried to plunge into the dense mass of thistles, so that he had the greatest difficulty in keeping his seat. Presently the Ostrich left him, and casting his eyes round he was astonished to see that all the young Ostriches were running about, scattered over the ground, while the Caranchos were pursuing, knocking down, and killing them. Meanwhile the old Ostrich was frantically rushing about trying to save them; but the Caranchos, when driven from one bird they were attacking, would merely rise and drop on the next one a dozen yards off; and as there were about fifteen Caranchos all engaged in the same way, the slaughter was proceeding at a great rate. My friend, who had been vainly struggling to get the better of his horse, was then forced to leave the place, and did not therefore see the end of the tragedy in which he had acted an involuntary part; but before going he saw that at least half the young birds were dead, and that these were all torn and bleeding on the small of the neck just behind the head, while in some cases the head had been completely wrenched off.

The Gauchos when snaring Partridges (Tinamus) frequently bribe the Caranchos to assist them. The snarer has a long slender cane with a small noose at the extremity, and when he sights a Partridge he gallops round it in circles until the bird crouches close in the grass; then the circles are narrowed and the pace slackened, while he extends the cane and lowers it gradually over the bewildered bird until the small noose is dropped over its head and it is caught. Many Partridges are not disposed to sit still to be taken in this open, barefaced way; but if the snarer keeps a Carancho hovering about by throwing him an occasional gizzard, the wariest Partridge is so stricken with fear that it will sit still and allow itself to be caught.

In the love season the male Caranchos are frequently seen fighting; and sometimes, when the battle is carried on at a great height in the air, the combatants are seen clasped together and falling swiftly towards the earth; but, in all contests I have witnessed, the birds have not been so blinded with passion as to fall the whole distance before separating. Besides these single combats, in which unpaired or jealous males engage in the love-season, there are at all times occasional dissensions amongst them, the cause of which it would be difficult to determine.

Here again, as often in hunting, the birds combine to punish an offender, and in some cases the punishment is death.

Their cry is exceedingly loud and harsh, a short abrupt note, like *cruk*, repeated twice; after which, if the bird is violently agitated, as when wounded or fighting, it throws its head backwards until the crown rests on the back, and rocks it from side to side, accompanying the action with a prolonged piercing cry of great power. This singular gesture of the Carancho, unique among birds, seems to express very forcibly a raging spirit.

The nest is built in a variety of situations: on trees, where there are any, but on the treeless pampas, where the Carancho is most at home, it is made on the ground, sometimes among the tall grass, while a very favourite site is a small islet or mound of earth rising well out of the water. When a suitable place has been found, the birds will continue to use the same nest for many consecutive years. It is a very large, slovenly structure of sticks, mixed with bones, pieces of skin, dry dung, and any portable object the bird may find to increase the bulk of his dwelling. The eggs are three or four, usually the last number, slightly oval, and varying greatly in colour and markings, some having irregular dark red blotches on a cream-coloured ground, while others are entirely of a deep brownish red, with a few black marks and blotches.

COCOI HERON

Ardea cocoi

Above grey; head, wings, and tail slatey black; beneath white; neck and sides striped with black; length 36 inches, wing 18 inches, tail 7 inches. Sexes alike.

THIS fine Heron is found throughout South and some parts of North America. In size, form, and colour it closely resembles the Common Heron of Europe; in flight, language, and feeding-habits the two species are identical, albeit inhabiting regions so widely separated. In the southern part of South America it is not seen associating with its fellows, nor does it breed in heronries; but this may be owing to the circumstance that in the temperate countries it is very thinly distributed; and it is highly probable, I think, that in the hotter regions, where it is more abundant, its habits may not appear so unsocial. Though they are always seen fishing singly, they pair for life, and male and female are never found far apart, but haunt the same stream or marsh all the year round. Azara says that in Paraguay, where they are rare, they go in pairs and breed in trees. On the pampas it makes its solitary nest amongst the rushes, and lays three blue eggs.

The following general remarks on the Heron apply chiefly to the *Ardea cocoi*, and to some extent also to other species of the Heron family.

I have observed Herons of several species a good deal, but chiefly the Cocoi, and think there is something to be said in support of Buffon's opinion that they are wretched, indigent birds, condemned by the imperfection of their organs to a perpetual struggle with want and misery. In reality the organs, and the correlated instincts, are just as perfect as in any other creature, but the Heron is certainly more highly specialised and lives more in a groove than most species. Consequently when food fails him in the accustomed channels he suffers more than most other species.

Much as the different species vary in size, from the *Ardea cocoi* to the diminutive Variegated Heron of Azara (*Ardetta involucris*), no bigger than a Snipe, there is yet much sameness in their conformation, language, flight, nesting and other habits. They possess a snake-like head and neck, and a sharp taper beak, with which they transfix their prey as with a dart—also the serrate claw, about which so much has been said, and which has been regarded as an instance of pure adaptation.

A curious circumstance has come under my observation regarding Herons. Birds in poor condition are very much infested with vermin; whether the vermin are the cause or effect of the poor condition, I do not know; but such is the fact. Now in this region (the Argentine Republic) Herons are generally very poor, a good-conditioned bird being a very rare exception; a majority of individuals are much emaciated and infested with intestinal worms; yet I have never found a bird infested with lice, though the Heron would seem a fit subject for them, and in the course of my rambles I have picked up many individuals apparently perishing from inanition. I do not wish to insinuate a belief that this immunity from vermin is due to the pectinated claw; for though the bird does scratch and clean itself with the claw it could never rid the entire plumage from vermin by this organ, which is as ill adapted for such a purpose as for " giving a firmer hold on its slippery prey."

The Spoonbill has also the serration, and is, unlike

the Heron, an active vigorous bird and usually fat ;
yet it is much troubled with parasites, and I have
found birds too weak to fly and literally swarming
with them.

I merely wish to call the attention of ornithologists to the fact that in the region where I have
observed Herons they are exempt in a remarkable
degree from external parasites.

Much has also been said about certain patches of
dense, clammy, yellowish down under the loose
plumage of Herons. These curious appendages may
be just as useless to the bird as the tuft of hair on
its breast is to the Turkey-cock ; but there are more
probabilities the other way, and it may yet be discovered that they are very necessary to its well-being.
Perhaps these clammy feathers contain a secretion
fatal to the vermin by which birds of sedentary
habits are so much afflicted, and from which Herons
appear to be so strangely free. They may even be
the seat of that mysterious phosphorescent light
which some one has affirmed emanates from the
Heron's breast when it fishes in the dark, and which
serves to attract the fish, or to render them visible
to the bird. Naturalists have, I believe, dismissed
the subject of this light as a mere fable without any
foundation of fact ; but real facts regarding habits
of animals have not infrequently been so treated.
Mr. Bartlett's interesting observations on the Flam-
ingoes in the Society's Gardens show that the ancient
story of the Pelican feeding its young on its own
blood is perhaps only a slightly embellished account
of a common habit of the Flamingo.

I have not observed Herons fishing by night very
closely, but there is one fact which inclines me to
believe it probable that some species might possess
the light-emitting power in question. I am convinced

that the *Ardea cocoi* sees as well by day as other diurnal species; the streams on the level pampas are so muddy that a fish two inches below the surface is invisible to the human eye, yet in these thick waters the Herons fish by night and by day. If the eye is adapted to see well with the bright sun shining, how can it see at night and in such unfavourable circumstances without some such extraneous aid to vision as the attributed luminosity?

Herons of all birds have the slowest flight; but though incapable of progressing rapidly when flying horizontally, when pursued by a Hawk the Heron performs with marvellous ease and grace an aerial feat unequalled by any other bird, namely that of rising vertically to an amazing height in the air. The swift vertical flight with which the pursued ascends until it becomes a mere speck in the blue zenith, the hurried zigzag flight of the pursuer, rising every minute above its prey, only to be left below again by a single flap of the Heron's wings, forms a sight of such grace, beauty, and power as to fill the mind of the spectator with delight and astonishment.

When the enemy comes to close quarters, the Heron instinctively throws itself belly up to repel the assault with its long, crooked, cutting claws. Raptorial species possess a similar habit; and the analogous correlation of habit and structure in genera so widely separated is very curious. The Falcon uses its feet to strike, lacerate, and grasp its prey; the Heron to anchor itself firmly to its perch; but for weapons of defence they are equally well adapted, and are employed in precisely the same manner. The Heron, with its great length of neck and legs, its lean unballasted body, large wings, and superabundance of plumage, is the least suited of birds to perch high ; yet the structure of the feet renders it perfectly safe for the bird to do so. Thus the Heron is enabled to sit on a smooth enamelled rush or on the summit of a tree, and doze securely in a wind that, were its feet formed like those of other Waders, would blow it away like a bundle of dead feathers.

Another characteristic of Herons is that they carry the neck, when flying, folded in the form of the letter S. At other times the bird also carries the neck this way ; and it is, indeed, in all long-necked species the figure the neck assumes when the bird reposes or is in the act of watching something below it ; and the Heron's life is almost a perpetual watch. Apropos of this manner of carrying the neck, so natural to the bird, is it not the cause of the extreme wariness observable in Herons? Herons are, I think, everywhere of a shy disposition ; with us they are the wildest of water-fowl, yet there is no reason for their being so, since they are never persecuted.

Birds ever fly reluctantly from danger ; and all species possessing the advantage of a long neck, such as the Swan, Flamingo, Stork, Spoonbill, etc., will continue with their necks stretched to their utmost capacity watching an intruder for an hour at a time rather than fly away. But in the Herons it must be only by a great effort that the neck can be wholly unbent ; for even if the neck cut out from a dead bird be forcibly straightened and then released, it flies back like a piece of india-rubber to its original shape. Therefore the effort to straighten the neck, invariably the first expression of alarm and curiosity, must be a painful one ; and to keep it for any length of time in that position is probably as insupportable to the bird as to keep the arm straightened vertically would be to a man. Thus the Heron flies at the first sight of an intruder, whilst the persecuted Duck, Swan, or other fowl continues motionless, watching

with outstretched neck, participating in the alarm
certainly, but not enduring actual physical pain.

Doubtless in many cases habits react upon and
modify the structure of parts; and in this instance
the modified structure has in its turn apparently
reacted on and modified the habits. In seeking for
and taking food, the body is required to perform
certain definite motions and assume repeatedly the
same attitudes; this is most frequently the case in
birds of aquatic habits. A readiness for assuming at
all times, and an involuntary falling into, these
peculiar attitudes and gestures appears to become
hereditary; and the species in which they are the
most noticeable seem incapable of throwing the habit
or manner off, even when placed in situations where
it is useless or even detrimental. *Tringæ* rapidly
peck and probe the mud as they advance; Plovers
peck and run, peck and run again. Now I have
noticed scores of times that these birds cannot possibly
lay aside this habit of pecking as they advance; for
even a wounded Plover running from his pursuer
over dry barren ground goes through the form of
eating by pausing for a moment every yard or so,
pecking the ground, then running on again.

The Paraguay Snipe, and probably other true
Snipes, possesses the singular habit of striking its
beak on the ground when taking flight. In this
instance has not the probing motion, performed
instinctively as the bird moves, been utilised to assist
it in rising?

Grebes on land walk erect like Penguins and have
a slow, awkward gait; and whenever they wish to
accelerate their progress they throw themselves forward on the breast and strike out the feet as in
swimming.

The Glossy Ibis feeds in shallow water, thrusting

its great sickle beak into the weeds at the bottom at every step. When walking on land it observes these motions, and seems incapable of progressing without plunging its beak downwards into imaginary water at every stride.

The Spoonbill wades up to its knees and advances with beak always immersed, and swaying itself from side to side, so that at each lateral movement of the body the beak describes a great semicircle in the water; a flock of these birds feeding reminds one of a line of mowers mowing grass. On dry ground the Spoonbill seems unable to walk directly forward like other birds, but stoops, keeping the body in a horizontal position, and, turning from side to side, sweeps the air with its beak, as if still feeding in the water.

In the foregoing instances (and I could greatly multiply them) in which certain gestures and movements accompany progressive motion, it is difficult to see how the structure can be in any way modified by them; but the preying attitude of the heron, the waiting motionless in perpetual readiness to strike, has doubtless given the neck its peculiar form.

Two interesting traits of the Heron (and they have a necessary connection) are its tireless watchfulness and its insatiable voracity; for these characteristics have not, I think, been exaggerated even by the most sensational of ornithologists.

In birds of other genera repletion is invariably followed by a period of listless inactivity during which no food is taken or required. But the Heron digests his food so rapidly that, however much he devours, he is always ready to gorge again; consequently he is not benefited so much by what he eats, and appears in the same state of semi-starvation when food is abundant as in times of scarcity. An old naturalist has suggested, as a reason for this, that the Heron, from its peculiar manner of taking its prey, requires fair weather to fish—that during spells of bad weather, when it is compelled to suffer the pangs of famine inactive, it contracts a meagre consumptive habit of body, which subsequent plenty cannot remove. A pretty theory, but it will not hold water; for in this region spells of bad weather are brief and infrequent; moreover, all other species that feed at the same table with the Heron, from the little flitting Kingfisher to the towering Flamingo, become excessively fat at certain seasons, and are at all times so healthy and vigorous that, compared with them, the Heron is the mere ghost of a bird. In no extraneous circumstances, but in the organisation of the bird itself, must be sought the cause of its anomalous condition; it does not appear to possess the fat-elaborating power, for at no season is any fat found on its dry, starved flesh; consequently there is no provision for a rainy day, and the misery of the bird (if it is miserable) consists in its perpetual, never-satisfied craving for food.

WHISTLING HERON
Ardea sibilatrix, Temm.

WHISTLING HERON

Ardea sibilatrix

Above grey; cap, crest, and wings greyish black; a rufous patch behind the eye; upper wing-coverts rufous; beneath white, with yellowish tinge on breast; beak reddish. Length 22 inches. Female similar.

THIS is a beautiful bird, with plumage as soft as down to the touch. Its colours are clear blue-grey and pale yellow, the under surface being nearly white. In some specimens that I have obtained the rump and tail-coverts had a pure primrose hue. There is a chestnut mark on the side of the head; the eye is white, and the legs dark green in life.

Azara named this Heron *Flauta del Sol* (Flute of the Sun), a translation of the Indian term *Curahi-remimbi*, derived from the popular belief that its whistling notes, which have a melodious and melancholy sound, prophesy changes in the weather.

It comes as far south as Buenos Ayres, but is only a summer visitor there, and very scarce. Having seen but little of it myself, I can only repeat Azara's words concerning it. He says it is common in Paraguay, going in pairs or families, and perches and roosts on trees, and when flying flaps its wings more rapidly than other Herons. It makes its nest on a tree, and lays two clear blue eggs.

I saw less of the Whistling or "Fluting" Heron than of any of the seven species I was acquainted with in La Plata. About its habits I found out nothing, and on that account I should have omitted all mention of it—that being the rule in this book—if its strange beauty had not charmed and made a lasting impression on my mind. The stuffed specimens, from

which the description is taken, do not show the
colours of the living bird—the soft clear grey and
primrose yellow—most delicate colours and rarely
seen in a bird of this size. In the museum specimens
the primrose yellow fades to white with a dull
yellowish tinge.

LITTLE RED HERON

Ardetta involucris

Above light fulvous, a black stripe on the nape; front, stripe on back of the neck, bend of wing and outer secondaries, chestnut-red; back striped with black; wing-feathers ash-grey with red tips; beneath yellowish white striped with brown; beak yellow, feet green; length 13, wing 5 inches.

THE Little Red, or Variegated, Heron which inhabits Paraguay and Argentina, is the least of the family to which it belongs, its body being no bigger than that of the Common Snipe; but in structure it is like other Herons, except that its legs are a trifle shorter in proportion to its size and its wings very much shorter than in other species. The under plumage is dull yellow in colour, while all the other parts are variegated with marks of fuscous and various shades of brown and yellow. The body is extremely slim, and the lower portion of the neck covered with thick plumage, giving that part a deceptively massive appearance. The perching faculty, possessed in so eminent a degree by all Herons, probably attains its greatest perfection in this species, and is combined with locomotion in a unique and wonderful manner. It inhabits beds of rushes growing in rather deep water; very seldom, and probably only accidentally, does it visit the shore, and only when driven up does it rise above the rushes; for its flight, unlike that of its congeners, is extremely feeble. The rushes it lives amongst rise, smooth as polished pipe-stems, vertically from water too deep for the bird to wade in; yet it goes up to the summit and down to the surface, moving freely and briskly about amongst them, or runs in a straight line through them almost as rapidly as a Plover can run over the bare level ground. Unless I myself had been a witness of this feat I could scarcely have credited it; for how does it manage to grasp the smooth vertical stems quickly and firmly enough to progress so rapidly without ever slipping down through them?

The Variegated Heron is a silent, solitary bird, found everywhere in the marshes along the Plata, as also in the rush- and sedge-beds scattered over the pampas. It breeds amongst the rushes, and lays from three to five spherical eggs, of a rich lively green and beautiful beyond comparison. The nest is a slight platform structure about a foot above the water, and so small that there is barely space enough on it for the eggs, which are large for the bird. When one looks down on them they cover and hide the slight nest, and being green like the surrounding rushes they are not easy to detect.

When driven up the bird flies eighty or a hundred yards away, and drops again amongst the rushes; it is difficult to flush it a second time, and a third time it is impossible. A curious circumstance is that where it finally settles it can never be found. As I could never succeed in getting specimens when I wanted them, I once employed some gaucho boys, who had dogs trained to hunt flappers, to try for this little Heron. They procured several specimens, and said that without the aid of their dogs they could never succeed in finding a bird, though they always marked the exact spot where it alighted. This I attributed to the slender figure it makes, and to the colour of the plumage so closely assimilating to that of the dead yellow and brown-spotted rushes always found amongst the green ones; but I did not know for many years that the bird possessed a

marvellous instinct that made its peculiar conformation and imitative colour far more advantageous
than they could be of themselves.

One day in November when out shooting, I noticed
a Variegated Heron stealing off quickly through a
bed of bulrushes, thirty or forty yards from me ;
he was a foot or so above the ground, and went so
rapidly that he appeared to glide through the rushes
without touching them.   I fired, but afterwards
ascertained that in my hurry I had missed my aim.

The bird, however, disappeared at the report ; and
thinking I had killed him I went to the spot.

It was a small, isolated bed of rushes I had seen
him in ;   the mud below and for some distance
round was quite bare and hard, so that it would
have been impossible for the bird to escape without
being perceived ;   and yet, dead or alive, he was not
to be found.   After vainly searching and re-searching
through the rushes for a quarter of an hour I gave
over the quest in great disgust and bewilderment,
and, after reloading, was just turning to go, when
behold ! there stood my Heron on a rush, no more
than eight inches from, and on a level with, my
knees.   He was perched, the body erect, and the
point of the tail touching the rush grasped by its
feet ; the long slender tapering neck was held stiff,
straight and vertically ;   and the head and beak,
instead of being carried obliquely, were also pointing
up.   There was not, from his feet to the tip of his
beak, a perceptible curve or inequality, but the whole
was the figure (the exact counterpart) of a straight
tapering rush : the loose plumage arranged to fill
inequalities, and the wings pressed into the hollow
sides, made it impossible to see where the body
ended and the neck began, or to distinguish head
from neck or beak from head.   This was, of course,

a front view; and the entire under surface of the bird was thus displayed, all of a uniform dull yellow, like that of a faded rush. I regarded the bird wonderingly for some time; but not the least motion did it make. I thought it was wounded or paralysed with fear, and, placing my hand on the point of its beak, forced the head down till it touched the back; when I withdrew my hand up flew the head, like a steel spring, to its first position. I repeated the experiment many times with the same result, the very eyes of the bird appearing all the time rigid and unwinking like those of a creature in a fit. What wonder that it is so difficult, almost impossible, to discover the bird in such an attitude! But how happened it that while repeatedly walking round the bird through the rushes I had not caught sight of the striped back and the broad dark-coloured sides? I asked myself this question, and stepped round to get a side view, when, *mirabile dictu*, I could still see nothing but the rush-like front of the bird! His motions on the perch, as he turned slowly or quickly round, still keeping the edge of the blade-like body before me, corresponded so exactly with my own that I almost doubted that I had moved at all. No sooner had I seen the finishing part of this marvellous instinct of self-preservation (this last act making the whole complete) than such a degree of delight and admiration possessed me as I have never before experienced during my researches, much as I have conversed with wild animals in the wilderness, and many and perfect as are the instances of adaptation I have witnessed. I could not finish admiring, and thought that never had anything so beautiful fallen in my way before; for even the sublime cloud-seeking instinct of the White Egret and the typical Herons seemed less admirable than this; and for some time I continued experimenting, pressing down the bird's head and trying to bend him by main force into some other position ; but the strange rigidity remained unrelaxed, the fixed attitude unchanged. I also found, as I walked round him, that as soon as I got to the opposite side and he could no longer twist himself on his perch, he whirled his body with great rapidity the other way, instantly presenting the same front as before.

Finally I plucked him forcibly from the rush and perched him on my hand, upon which he flew away ; but he flew only fifty or sixty yards off, and dropped into the dry grass. Here he again put in practice the same instinct so ably that I groped about for ten or twelve minutes before refinding him, and was astonished that a creature to all appearance so weak and frail should have strength and endurance sufficient to keep its body rigid and in one attitude for so long a time.

Some recent or at all events later observations appear to show that some species of Bittern possess a similar instinct to that of the bird described—the faculty of effacing themselves as it were in the presence of an enemy. Doubtless any Bittern, its colouring being what it is, would make itself invisible among partially decayed and dead vegetation by extending and stiffening its body and keeping its breast towards its intruder. The peculiar thing in the case of the small Heron is that the whole action of the bird appears to be framed and designed expressly to make it look exactly like a dead yellow tapering bulrush.

But what can one say of such an instinct—if we can call it an instinct ? It is in its essence a weakness in the creature similar to that of many mammals, birds, fishes, batrachians, reptiles and insects that become paralysed with fear, or rather hypnotised, in the presence of an enemy. A strange flaw in the animal, since it brings to naught all the admirable instincts of self-preservation it has been endowed with, and gives it, without a struggle, a prey to its enemies, even to those of a slow, sluggish disposition.

In this particular instance the weakness or fault of nature has been taken advantage of by that principle which we call natural selection and has resulted in a more perfect protection than if the bird had been incapable of losing its mind, as one may say. In other words, the creature's liability to the hypnotic or cataleptic state on certain occasions is its best protection.

This, however, is not the only case in which a seemingly fatal weakness has been turned to good account, as we see in the death-like swoon, or " pretending to be dead," of many creatures when overcome by or in the presence of an enemy. I have observed it in the pampas fox and opossum, in the Tinamu, the Partridge of South America, in our Corncrake, and other Rails, and I have captured small birds by giving them a sudden fright.

By a strange chance I discovered that my Little Bittern was also subject to this weakness. A gaucho boy of my acquaintance, knowing that I was interested in this bird, one day brought me a dead specimen. He said he had flushed it from a rush-bed, and as the bird flew away over dry land, he gave chase, and soon ran it down and captured it ; but though perfectly uninjured it quickly died in his hand. As it was too late in the evening for me to deal with it I put it in a cage which had once been used to keep a Cardinal Finch in and hung it up under the veranda where it would be safe from cats. Next morning to my very great astonishment it was gone ! A long-dead bird in a closed cage hung high up out of the way for safety, and now it was not there ! How explain such a thing ? There was no possible explanation, and it made me perfectly miserable for days thinking of it. Then at last it dawned on my weary brain that my dead bird had been alive all the time, that life had at all events come back to it, and that by squeezing its thin body edgeways through the wire it made its escape. Yet the wires were close enough to keep a Cardinal in confinement !

BLACK-FACED IBIS
Theristicus caudatus (Bodd.)

BLACK-FACED IBIS

Theristicus caudatus

Sides of throat and lores bare, skin black; top of head and lower part of neck in front reddish chestnut; neck white; back and wings grey with green reflections; tertials and outer webs of secondaries for two-thirds of their length white, remainder dark green; primaries dark green; rump light green, bronzed; tail dark bronze green; under parts black; length 33, wing 16.25 inches.

THIS very fine Ibis, called *Mandurria ó Curucáu* by Azara and *Vandúria de invierno* (Winter Vanduria) in the vernacular, is one of the most interesting winter visitors from Patagonia to the pampas of Buenos Ayres. It is found in Chili, and has even been obtained as far north as Peru. On the east side of the continent it is most abundant (during the cold season) about latitude 37 deg. or 38 deg. Its summer home and breeding ground appears to be in the extreme south of the continent, its eggs having been obtained on the Straits of Magellan by Darwin, and later by Dr. Cunningham, who only says of it that it is a shy and wary bird, that goes in flocks of from four to eight, and has a cry resembling *qua-qua, qua-qua*. But he might just as well have spelt it *quack-quack*, since *qua-qua* fails to give the faintest idea of the series of hard, abrupt notes of extraordinary power the bird utters, usually when on the wing, which sound like blows of a powerful hammer on a metal plate. On the pampas this Ibis appears in May, frequents dry grassy situations, and goes in flocks of a dozen to forty or fifty individuals. They walk rapidly, stooping very much, and probing the ground with their long, slender, curved beaks, and appear to subsist principally on the larvæ of the large horned beetle, with which their stomachs are usually found filled. So intent are they on seeking their food that the members of a flock often scatter in all directions and wander quite out of sight of each other; when this happens they occasionally utter loud vehement cries, as if to call their companions, or to inform each other of their whereabouts. Frequently one is seen to lift up its wings as if to fly, and, stretching them up vertically, to remain for fifteen or twenty seconds in this curious attitude. At sunset they all rise up clamouring and direct their flight to the nearest watercourse, and often on their way thither go through a strange and interesting performance. The flock suddenly precipitates itself downwards with a violence wonderful to see, each bird rushing this way and that as if striving to outvie its fellows in every wild fantastic motion of which they are capable. In this manner they rise and descend again and again, sometimes massed together, then scattering wide apart in all directions. This exercise they keep up for some time, and while it lasts they make the air resound for miles with their loud percussive screams.

In Patagonia I first observed this Ibis roosting on tall trees; and, according to Azara, it possesses the same habit in Paraguay. He says that all the flocks within a circuit of some leagues resort to one spot to sleep, and prefer tall dead trees, bordering on the water, and if there is only one suitable tree all the birds crowd on to it, and in the morning scatter, each family or pair flying away to spend the day in its customary feeding-ground.

The egg obtained by Dr. Cunningham at Elizabeth Island is thus described by Prof. Newton (*Ibis*, 1870, p. 502): "Dull surface of a pale greenish white with engrained blotches (mostly small) of neutral tint, and some few blotches, spots, and specks of dull deep brown ; towards the larger end some hair-like streaks of a lighter shade of the same, and so far having an Ibidine or Plataleine character."

CRESTED SCREAMER

Chauna chavaria

Slatey grey, darker on the back; chin, neck, and cheeks whitish; a naked ring round the neck; nape crested; belly pale grey; feet red; length 32, wing 19 inches.

THIS majestic bird, called *Chaja* in the vernacular, is common throughout the Plata district, in marshes and on the open level country abounding in water and succulent grasses, and ranges south to the neighbourhood of Bahia Blanca. It is most abundant on the pampas south of Buenos Ayres city, and on that vast expanse of perfectly level green country the bird is seen at its best; it is there an important feature in the landscape; its vocal performances are doubly impressive on account of the profound silence of nature, and its singularity—the contrast between its aerial habit and ponderous structure—strikes one more forcibly where the view is so unobstructed and the atmosphere so pure.

The Crested Screamer, like most of the larger birds and mammals in every part of the globe to which European emigration is attracted, is probably doomed to rapid extermination. My observations of the bird, in that portion of the pampas where it is most abundant, date back some years, to a time when the inhabitants were few and mainly of Spanish race, never the destroyers of bird-life. The conditions had become extremely favourable to this species. It is partially aquatic in its habits; and in desert places is usually found in marshes, wading in the shallow water, and occasionally swimming to feed on the seeds and succulent leaves of water-loving plants. After the old giant grasses of the pampas had been eaten up by the cattle, and the sweet grasses of Europe had taken their place, the Screamers took kindly to that new food, preferring the clovers, and seemed as terrestrial in their feeding-habits as Upland Geese. Their food was abundant, and they were never persecuted by the natives. Their flesh is very dark, is coarse-grained but good to eat, with a flavour resembling that of Wild Duck, and there is a great deal of meat on a bird with a body larger than that of a Swan. Yet no person ever thought of killing or eating the Chaja ; and the birds were permitted to increase to a marvellous extent. It was a common thing a few years ago in the dry season to see them congregated in thousands ; and so little afraid of man were they that I have often ridden through large scattered flocks without making the birds take wing.

A curious thing about the Screamer is that it pairs for life, and yet is one of the most social of birds. But if a large flock is closely looked at, the birds are invariably seen methodically ranged in pairs. Another curious thing is that, notwithstanding the formidable weapons they possess (each wing being armed with two large spurs), they are extremely pacific in temper. I have never been able to detect even the slightest approach to a quarrel among them ; yet it is hard to believe that they do not fight sometimes, since weapons of offence are usually found correlated with the disposition to use them. Captive birds, however, can be made to fight ; and I have known gauchos take them for the pleasure of witnessing their battles. They are very easily tamed, and in that state seem to show greater docility and intelligence than any of our domestic birds ; and become so attached to their home that it is quite safe to allow them to fly about at will. They associate, but do not quarrel, with the poultry. They are quick to distinguish strangers from the people of the house, showing considerable suspicion of them, and sometimes raising a loud alarm at a stranger's approach. Towards dogs and cats they are often unfriendly; and when they are breeding it is dangerous for a strange person to approach the nest, as they will sometimes attack him with the greatest fury.

The Screamer is a very heavy bird, and rises from the ground laboriously, the wings, as in the case of the Swan, making a loud noise. Nevertheless it loves soaring, and will rise in an immense spiral until it wholly disappears from sight in the zenith, even in the brightest weather; and considering its great bulk and dark colour, the height it ultimately attains must be very great. On sunny, windless days, especially in winter and spring, they often spend hours at a time in these sublime aerial exercises, slowly floating round and round in vast circles, and singing at intervals. How so heavy and comparatively short-winged a bird can sustain itself for such long periods in the thin upper air to which it rises has not yet been explained.

The voice is very powerful. When disturbed, or when the nest is approached, both birds utter at intervals a loud alarm-cry, resembling in sound the anger-cry of the Peacock, but twice as loud. At other times its voice is exercised in a kind of singing performance, in which male and female join, and which produces the effect of harmony. The male begins, the female takes up her part, and then with marvellous strength and spirit they pour forth a torrent of strangely-contrasted sounds—some bassoon-like in their depth and volume, some like drum-beats, and others long, clear, and ringing. It is the loudest animal-sound of the pampas, and its jubilant, martial character strongly affects the mind in that silent, melancholy wilderness.

The Screamers sing all the year round, at all hours, both on the ground and when soaring ; when in pairs the two birds invariably sing together, and when in flocks they sing in concert. At night they are heard about nine o'clock in the evening, and again just before dawn. It is not unusual, however, to hear them singing at other hours.

The nest is a large fabric placed among the low rushes and water-lilies, and is sometimes seen floating on the water, away from its moorings. The eggs are five, pointed at one end, pure white, and in size like the eggs of the domestic Goose. The young are clothed in yellow down like goslings, and follow the parents about from the date of hatching.

BLACK-NECKED SWAN

Cygnus nigricollis

White; head and neck black; postocular stripe and chin white; lores naked; bill plumbeous, cere red. Length 48, wing 17 inches. Female similar.

To my perhaps partial mind this species is pre-eminent for beauty among the Swans, although it is considerably smaller than the bird of the Old World, and does not, it must be admitted, comport itself so majestically. In questions of this kind it is natural for every one to be somewhat biassed in favour of the things of his own country; but it will be readily admitted by all, I think, that the black-necked bird is one of three species greatly surpassing all others of this genus in beauty—the other two being, of course, the domesticated Swan of Europe and the Australian Black Swan (the most graceful of Swans).

This Swan is very abundant on the pampas of Buenos Ayres and in Patagonia, and ranges south to the Magellan Straits and the Falklands. As a rule they are seen in small flocks, but sometimes as many as two or three hundred congregate together. They are heavy birds and rise with difficulty, and fly rapidly and with great violence, like all heavy-bodied short-winged species; but in no other very large bird with which I am acquainted do the wings produce so loud a rushing sound. In quiet places the beating of their wings can be heard distinctly when the birds are no longer in sight, although, owing to their large size, the eye can follow them very far. Gauchos sometimes capture them by suddenly charging down the wind upon them, uttering loud shouts which greatly terrify the birds, and when they attempt to rise with the wind they only flap along the ground and are easily knocked over. A gaucho of my acquaintance one day caught three out of a flock of six in this way; but a very strong wind favoured him, and the birds were at some distance from the water, and allowed him to come near before making the sudden charge.

According to Mr. Gibson, who has observed their breeding-habits, they begin to nest in July—just after the winter solstice. The nest is always placed among thick rushes growing in deep water, and the Swan invariably swims to and from her nest. It is built up from the bottom of the swamp, in some instances four or five feet deep, and rises a foot and a half above the surface. The top of the nest measures about two feet across, with a slight hollow for the eggs, which are cream-coloured and have a smooth glossy shell. The number varies from three to five, and on one occasion six were found. Mr. Gibson has seen the parent bird swimming from the nest with the young on her back.

BRAZILIAN TEAL
Querquedula brazilienis (Gm.)

BRAZILIAN TEAL

Querquedula brasiliensis

Above brown; head more rufous; lower back, tail, and lesser wing-coverts black; wings brownish black; outer webs of inner primaries and the secondaries shining bronze-green; broad tips of outer secondaries white, divided from the green area by a black band; beneath paler, breast washed with rusty red; bill and feet orange; length 15.5, wing 7 inches.

THIS richly coloured Teal, which is widely extended in South America from Guiana down to the Straits of Magellan, is usually met with in pairs near Buenos Ayres, although as many as five or six are sometimes seen together. In habits it is a tree-Duck, preferring water-courses in the neighbourhood of woods, and is frequently seen perched on horizontal branches. The flight is slow and with the wings very much depressed, as in a Duck about to alight on the water; and the beautiful blue, green, and white speculum is thus rendered very conspicuous. The note of the male in the love-season is a long, plaintive whistle, singularly pure and sweet in sound, and heard usually in the evening.

It is a rather curious coincidence that the vernacular name of this Teal in La Plata should be *Pato Portugués*, which means, as things are understood in that region, Brazilian Duck.

BROWN PINTAIL

Dafila spinicauda

Above brown; feathers black in the centre and margined with brown; head above bright rufous spotted with black; wings brown, with a large speculum of bronzy black, distinctly margined above and below with buff; beneath, throat dirty white, sparingly spotted with black; breast, flanks, and crissum tinged with rufous, the feathers with black centres; belly white, in the lower portion slightly varied with brown; bill black, at the base yellow; feet plumbeous; length 19, wing 9.7 inches.

THE Brown Pintail is the commonest Duck in the Argentine Republic, and unites in the largest flocks. It is also, according to Philippi and Landbeck, the commonest species in Chili. It ranges from South Brazil and Peru to the Magellan Straits and the Falklands; but is probably most abundant in the Plata district and in North Patagonia. In the autumn it sometimes visits the pampas in immense numbers, to feed on the seed of the giant thistle (*Carduus mariana*); and on these occasions I have known as many as sixty killed at one shot. The birds, however, soon become wary when feeding on the open plains in large flocks, and it then becomes impossible to approach them without a trained horse. The Ducks pay no attention to horses and cattle browsing near them; and the trained animal, with the gunner concealing his gun and person behind it, feeds quietly along, and gradually approaches the flock until within range. In the valley of the Rio Negro, in Patagonia, the Pintails sometimes cause serious damage to the farmers, coming up in clouds from the river by night to devour the ripe grain.

In favourable seasons the Pintail is a resident; but like the Marsh-Gulls, Pigeons, the American

Golden Plover, and all birds that live and move in immense bodies, it travels often and far in search of food or water. A season of scarcity will quickly cause them to disappear from the pampas; and sometimes, after an absence of several months, a day's rain will end with the familiar sound of their cry and the sight of their long trains winging their way across the darkening heavens.

Their nest is made on the ground, under the grass or thistles, at a distance from the water, and is plentifully lined with down plucked from the bosom of the sitting bird. The eggs are seven or eight in number and of a deep cream-colour.

WHITE-FACED PINTAIL

Dafila bahamensis

Above reddish brown; feather centres blackish; tail and upper tail-coverts fawn; wings slatey black; broad speculum bronze-green, with fawn margin above and below; edging of external secondaries fawn; beneath brownish fawn, covered with concealed black spots; throat, cheeks, and front white; bill dark with a crimson patch at the base in each side; feet dark; length 18, wing 8.4 inches. Female similar.

SOMEONE in the eighteenth century picked up a dead Duck of an unknown species on the seashore in the Bahama Islands; it was then sent to a naturalist in Europe who had the naming of all the creatures, and quite naturally he gave it the name of *Bahamensis*. And although we know that the duck does not inhabit the Bahamas, but is found throughout South America from British Guiana to Patagonia, and that it is one of the commonest Ducks in Brazil, there is a wise ornithological rule which forbids us, while the world endures, to call it anything but the Bahama Duck or Pintail. I was obliged to give it that name in *Argentine Ornithology,* but I think readers of this book in South America will henceforth prefer to call it by the name I have given it here. Doubtless there are other Pintail Ducks with white faces, but this has not given a name to any other species. The Brown Pintail is our most abundant species in Argentina, and I have noticed in flocks of great size, sometimes of many thousands, of that duck, that a single White-faced Duck in the flock could be detected at a long distance by means of that same snowy whiteness of the face.

On the Pampas and Patagonia it is not a common Duck and is almost invariably seen in pairs. I have, however, sometimes seen three or four together.

ARGENTINE WOOD-PIGEON

Columba picazuro

Above pale brown; head and neck vinous; back of neck with white cross-bands which are edged with black; lower back and tail plumbeous; wings plumbeous, larger coverts broadly edged with white; beneath pale vinaceous; flanks and crissum plumbeous; length 14 inches, wing 8 inches. Female similar.

THIS bird so closely resembles the European Wood-Pigeon in its appearance, habits, and language that I prefer in this book to drop the name of Picazuro Pigeon used in the former work (*Argentine Ornithology*) and call it the Argentine Wood-Pigeon. The chief differences are the absence of the white collar and the strangely human-like sound of its notes.

In summer they inhabit woods, and are seen in pairs or small parties, but in winter unite in flocks of from twenty to one or two hundred individuals, and roam much over the open country. It is a wary bird, and when feeding walks on the ground in a slow, somewhat stately manner. In spring its song resounds in the woods, and, when heard for the first time, fills the listener with wonder, so human-like in tone are its long, mournful notes. The notes are five, the last one prolonged, with a falling inflection, and profoundly sorrowful. The nest is a platform structure, frequently placed on a broad horizontal branch; the eggs are two, and closely resemble those of the common Rock-Dove of Europe.

SPOTTED DOVE

Zenaida maculata

Above pale brown; nape plumbeous; outer wing-coverts and scapularies with a few black spots; wings dark grey, with fine white margins; tail plumbeous, broadly ended with white, and crossed by a subapical black band; middle rectrices like the back; beneath pale vinaceous, brighter on the breast, and whiter on the throat; bill black, feet yellow; length 9, wing 5.5 inches. Female similar.

THIS is the commonest species of the Pigeon tribe in the Argentine country, and is known to everyone as the *Torcasa*, probably a corruption of *Tórtola* (Turtle-Dove). In autumn they often congregate in very large flocks, and are sometimes observed migrating, flock succeeding flock, all travelling in a northerly direction, and continuing to pass for several consecutive days. But these autumnal migrations are not witnessed every year, nor have I seen any return migration in spring; while the usual autumn and winter movements are very irregular, and apparently depend altogether on the supply of food. When the giant thistle has covered the plains in summer incredible numbers of Torcasas appear later in the season, and usually spend the winter on the plains, congregating every evening in countless myriads wherever there are trees enough to afford a suitable roosting-place.

On bright warm days in August, the sweet and sorrowful sob-like song of this Dove, composed of five notes, is heard from every grove—a pleasing, soft, murmuring sound, which causes one to experience by anticipation the languid summer feeling in his veins.

The nest, as in other Pigeons, is a simple platform of slender sticks; the eggs are oval, white, and two in number. The birds appear to breed by preference near a human habitation, and do so probably for the sake of the protection afforded them; for the Chimango and other birds of prey destroy their eggs and young to a large extent.

One summer a Torcasa laid an egg in the nest of one of my Pigeons, built on the large horizontal branch of a tree at some distance from the dovecote. The egg was hatched, and the young bird reared by its foster-parents; and when able to fly it took up its abode along with the other Pigeons. The following spring it began to separate itself from its companions, and would fly to the porch, and sit there cooing by the hour every day. At length it went away to the plantation, having, I believe, found a mate, and we saw no more of it.

YPECAHA RAIL

Aramides ypecaha

Above olive-green; neck red; front cinereous; rump and tail black; beneath, throat white, breast and neck cinereous; abdomen rosy red, lower belly and thighs grey; flanks and crissum black; under wing-coverts rufous, with black cross-bars; bill yellow, feet red; length 19, wing 8.5 inches. Female similar.

YPECAHA is the Guarani name, preserved by Azara, of this highly interesting species; by the Spanish it is called *Gallineta,* from its supposed resemblance to a fowl. Without any brilliant tints, there is yet something so pleasing to the eye in the various hues of its plumage—light brown and drab colour, grey, buff, and black—all these colours so harmoniously disposed, the effect heightened by the long, straight yellow beak, golden-red eye, and vermilion legs, that I do not know a handsomer waterfowl.

These Rails are found as far south as the thirty-fifth parallel of latitude, and are abundant along the marshy borders of the Plata, frequenting the vast reed-beds and forests of water-loving *Erythrina cristagalli.* Where they are never persecuted they are bold, pugnacious birds, coming out of the reeds by day and attacking the domestic poultry about the houses and even in the streets of the villages situated on the borders of their marshy haunts. But when they are compelled to place man on the list of their enemies, it is a difficult matter to get a sight of one; for, like all birds that rise laboriously, they are vigilant to excess, and keep themselves so well concealed that the sportsman may pass through their haunts every day of the year and the Ypecaha still be to him no

more than a "wandering voice." But even persecution does not obliterate a certain inquisitive boldness which characterises them. Usually they roam
singly in quest of food, but have reunions in the
evening and occasionally during the day, especially
in gloomy weather. On misty days they often wander
to a distance from the covert, walking with an easy,
somewhat stately grace, jerking the tail at every
stride, and running with a velocity no man can
equal. Where there are woods they usually fly when
disturbed into a tree ; and it is in connection with
this habit that the Ypecaha sometimes makes a
curious mistake in places where it has not been
much shot at. One day, while pushing my way
through a dense growth of rushes, I saw two Ypecahas
not fifteen yards from me, on the horizontal branch
of a tree, to which they had evidently flown for
safety. I was anxious to secure them, but surprised
at their temerity ; and wishing to find out its cause,
I approached them still nearer, and then stood for
some time observing them. It was easy to see that
they fancied themselves quite safe from me while
off the ground. In the most unconcerned manner
they continued strutting up and down along the
branch, jerking their tails, and turning about this
way and that, as if to tantalise their baffled enemy
by ostentatiously displaying their graces.

When surprised on the open ground the Ypecaha
lies close, like a Tinamu, refusing to rise until
almost trodden upon. It springs up with a loud-
sounding whirr, rushes violently through the air till,
gaining the reeds, it glides a few yards and then
drops ; its flight is thus precisely like that of the
Tinamu, and is more sounding and violent than
that of the Grouse or Partridge. On spying an
intruder it immediately utters a powerful cry, in

strength and intonation not unlike that of the Pea-fowl. This note of alarm is answered by other birds at a distance as they hastily advance to the spot where the warning was sounded. The cry is repeated at irregular intervals, first on one side, then on the other, as the birds change their position to dog the intruder's steps and inspect him from the reeds. I have surprised parties of them in an open space, and shot one or more; but no sooner had the sur-vivors gained their refuge than they turned about to watch and follow me, sounding their powerful alarm the whole time. I have frequently been followed half a mile through the rushes by them, and by lying close and mimicking their cries have always succeeded in drawing them about me.

But the Ypecaha's loudest notes of alarm are weak compared with the cries he utters at other times, when, untroubled with a strange presence, he pours out his soul in screams and shrieks that amaze the listener with their unparalleled power. These screams in all their changes and modulations have a resemblance to the human voice, but to the human voice exerted to its utmost pitch, and expressive of agony, frenzy, and despair. A long, piercing shriek, astonishing for its strength and vehemence, is suc-ceeded by a lower note, as if in the first one the creature had wellnigh exhausted itself. The double scream is repeated several times; then follow other sounds, resembling, as they rise and fall, half-sup-pressed cries of pain and moans of anguish. Suddenly the unearthly shrieks are renewed in all their power. This is kept up for some time, several birds scream-ing in concert; it is renewed at intervals throughout the day, and again at set of sun, when the woods and marshes resound with the extravagant uproar. I have said that several birds unite in screaming; this is invariably the case. I have enjoyed the rare pleasure of witnessing the birds at such times; and the screams then seem a fit accompaniment to their disordered gestures and motions.

A dozen or twenty birds have their place of reunion on a small area of smooth, clean ground surrounded by rushes or sedges; and by lying well concealed and exercising some patience, one is enabled to watch their proceedings. First one bird is heard to utter a loud metallic-sounding note, three times repeated, and somewhat like the call of the Guinea-fowl. It issues from the reeds or rushes, and is a note of invitation quickly responded to by other birds on every hand as they all hurriedly repair to the customary spot. In a few moments, and almost simultaneously, the birds appear, emerging from the reeds and running into the open space, where they all immediately wheel about and begin the exhibition.

Whilst screaming they rush from side to side as if possessed with frenzy, the wings spread and agitated, the beak wide open and raised vertically. I never observed them fight or manifest anger towards each other during these performances; and knowing the pugnacious spirit of the Ypecahas, and how ready they are to seek a quarrel with birds of other species, this at first surprised me, for I was then under the mistaken impression that these gatherings were in some way related to the sexual instinct.

Whilst watching them I also remarked another circumstance. When concealing myself amongst the rushes I have been compelled to place myself so disadvantageously, owing to the wet ground, that any single bird straying accidentally into the open space would have discovered my presence immediately; yet the birds have entered and finished their

performance without seeing me, so carried away
are they by the emotion that possesses them during
these moments. But no sooner has the wild chorus
ended, than, aware of my presence, they have fled
precipitately into the reeds.

We frequently speak of our familiarity with the
habits of the species we have long and carefully
observed in a state of nature ; yet the knowledge so
gained must necessarily be exceedingly imperfect, for
with many shy vigilant birds it is next to impossible
to see them without being seen ; and no bird, con-
scious of being watched, will act unconstrainedly
any more than a human being with clouded reputation will comport himself naturally with the eyes
of a detective on him. While we are observing
the bird, the bird watches us : of all its curious
doings when we are out of sight and mind we see
nothing. The only way to learn the habits of a species
like the Ypecaha—wary, intelligent, and passing its
life behind a screen of rushes—is to domesticate it ;
for although in this state some instincts are blunted
and others remain in abeyance, they are not obliter-
ated. It might surprise some that I speak of the
Ypecaha as an intelligent bird, since it is a member
of the " stupid family," as Professor Parker has called
the Rails ; but in spite of the very profound admiration I feel for that illustrious anatomist, I believe
he is wrong about these birds : there is, to my mind,
very much more stupidity in the Anserine and
Limicoline families, while the Ypecaha has always
seemed to me a singularly intelligent bird.

Fortunately Azara was able to give an account of
one of these birds in a domestic state, which shows
that it makes a very sprightly and entertaining although a mischievous pet. It was taken young and
allowed to run about at liberty with the poultry at

the house of a village doctor in Paraguay. When full-grown it was very domineering, and became the tyrant of the poultry-yard. Occasionally a cock had the courage to face it, and then a singular combat would ensue : the Ypecaha, moving with astonishing rapidity, putting its head low, would charge, and, thrusting its head between the cock's legs, fling him instantly on his back, then rain a shower of blows on his breast before he could rise. It was fond of eggs, and always knew when a hen went off to lay, cautiously following her to the nest and then concealing itself at some distance to wait. As soon as the egg was dropped it would run, pick it up with its beak, and carry it away to a safe distance, and then, breaking a hole in the shell at one end, suck out the contents without spilling a drop. Sometimes, when the hen remained too long on the nest, it would lose its temper, and, driving her off, pursue her with the greatest animosity about the grounds, administering correction with its sharp beak. Not satisfied with devouring all the eggs laid by the doctor's fowls, it visited all the neighbours' houses, doing so much damage that at length the poor doctor, afraid perhaps that his practice would suffer, had the troublesome bird put to death.

This Ypecaha would never allow any one to touch it, but it would come into the house and search through all the rooms for thimbles, scissors, and other small metal objects, and these it would carry away to conceal them among the weeds or else bury them in the mud. It was also a good mouser, and after killing a mouse with a blow from its beak would swallow it entire.

COMMON JACANA

Parra jacana (Linn.)

JACANA

Parra jacana

Head and neck purplish black; back and wings bright chestnut; primaries and secondaries pale greenish yellow tipped with brown; flanks dark chestnut; breast dark black; abdomen purplish; the tail chestnut tipped with black; wattles on head and base of bill red, rest of bill yellow; feet olive; length 10.5, wing 5.8 inches. Female similar.

THE beautiful Jacana—pronounced something like *Yasaná*—also called in the vernacular *Alas-amarillas* (Yellow-wings), differs very widely from all the other members of the Limicoline Order in which it is placed, in the enormously elongated toes which enable it to run about on the floating leaves of water plants. It is supposed to come nearest to the Plovers, but is more like a Rail in its appearance, which is most singular.

The colouring of the plumage heightens the singularity of its appearance : the head, neck, and underparts being black; the shoulders, back, and wing-coverts chestnut; while the quills, which have a bright satiny lustre, are apple-green in colour, and in some lights appear golden-yellow.

In the southern part of the Plata district the Jacana is migratory, arriving from the north in Buenos Ayres early in October, either singly or in small parties. In their migration they appear to follow the course of the Plata ; and though some individuals are found breeding inland, they are for the most part confined to the littoral marshes.

The Jacanas journey by very easy stages, frequently alighting to rest by the way ; for they are so incapable of sustained flight that boys on the pampas occasionally take them, pursuing them on horseback till the birds drop down exhausted. I believe the migratory Rails travel in the same way—a matter not easily determined, as they migrate by night; but they are feeble-winged creatures, and when driven to rise flutter away as if wounded. I have observed the Jacanas migrating by day, but would not for this reason affirm that they do not journey by night, since the Bartram's Sandpiper and other species journey both day and night.

The Jacana flies swiftly, in a straight line and close to the surface; the wings flutter rapidly, and there are frequent intervals of gliding. When rising it presents a most novel appearance, as the lovely golden-green of the wings is quite concealed when the bird is at rest; the beauty of its flight is thus greatly enhanced by the sudden display of a hue so rare and delicate. At a distance from the beholder, and in a strong sunshine, the wings appear of a shining golden yellow. Not only when flying does the Jacana make a display of its beautiful wings; without rising it has a way of exhibiting them, appearing to delight as much in them as the Cockatoo does in its crest or the Peacock in its train. When several of these birds live in company, occasionally they all in one moment leave their feeding, and with quick excited notes, and clustering together in a close group, go through a singular and pretty performance, all together holding their wings outstretched and agitated, some with a rapid fluttering, others with a slow-moving leisurely motion like that of a butterfly sunning itself. The performance over, the birds peaceably scatter again. I have never observed Jacanas fighting.

Shortly after arriving they pair, and build a simple nest with few materials, usually on the floating weeds.

The eggs are four, in shape like a Snipe's eggs, spotted with chestnut on a pale yellowish-brown ground. During incubation the male keeps guard at some distance from the nest, and utters a warning cry at the approach of an intruder ; the female instantly flies from the nest, but in rising renders herself very conspicuous. When the nest is approached the parent birds hover about, occasionally fluttering as if wounded, all the time keeping up a clamour of hurried, angry notes somewhat resembling the yelping cries of the Stilt.

SPUR-WING LAPWING

Vanellus cayennensis

Above grey; broad front and vertical crest black; patch on the scapulars purplish bronze; upper tail-coverts white; primaries purplish black; greater coverts white; lesser wing-coverts bronze green; tail, basal half white, the other half purple-black tipped with white; beneath, chin, line down the middle of the throat and breast shining black; sides of neck grey, passing into white on the face; abdomen and under wing-coverts white; bill, spur on wing, and feet red; eyes crimson; length 13, wing 8.2 inches. Female similar.

THE Lapwing of La Plata is considerably larger than the well-known Lapwing of the Old World, but closely resembles that bird in the general colour of the plumage, in the long, slender, black crest, and in general appearance. Throughout the Argentine country it is called *Téru-téru*, from its ever-repeated disyllabic cry; west of the Andes the vernacular name is *Queltrégua*, also in imitation of its notes. It has red legs, crimson irides, a rosy beak tipped with black, and coral-red wing-spurs; and these spots of bright colour add to its bold, striking appearance. In size, beauty, and spirit it is a king among the Plovers, while its jealous, aggressive disposition gives it the character of a tyrant amongst birds in general. On the pastoral pampas (the district from which the giant grasses have disappeared) it is (or was) excessively abundant; and it is there resident, although, as with most strong-winged resident species, some individuals do certainly migrate, small parties being occasionally seen in spring and autumn flying steadily at a great height, apparently performing a long journey. As a rule the birds pair for life, and remain always on the spot where they breed. They may be persecuted with guns, their eggs taken year after year, even the ground turned up with the plough, but they still refuse to be driven out. In regions having a broken surface—hills, woods, and sheltered hollows—birds naturally get attached to one spot, for each locality possesses its own features, and individuals frequenting it acquire a knowledge of its advantages. The vast pampas have a uniform level surface, and produce the same kinds of food in the same quantities. They are parched with droughts and flooded by rains alternately, and swept by dust storms in summer and cold gales in winter —violent enough, one would imagine, to drive every winged creature away and obliterate all marks of home. Again, the powerful flight of this species would enable it to take long journeys, and if un-affected by atmospheric changes, scarcity of food and water might be a temptation to seek new regions. But through all vicissitudes the Téru-téru clings to its chosen spot of ground.

In defence of its territory it wages perpetual war against most living creatures, the objects of its special abhorrence being men, dogs, Rheas, and birds of prey generally. Its noisy cry and irascible temper are spoken of by most travellers and naturalists; for no person riding across the pampas could possibly overlook the bird, with its screaming protests against all trespassers perpetually ringing in his ears; but they have all omitted to mention the singular habit which this bird has of associating in sets of three for the purpose of amusement or play. Each couple, as I have said, live always together on their own pretty well-defined plot of ground, which they jealously guard from intrusion. Yet if you watch a pair of them for a while you will presently see another bird—one of a neighbouring couple—rise up and fly to them, leaving his own mate to take care of home; and instead of resenting this visit as an intrusion, they welcome it with notes and signs of manifest pleasure. Advancing to the visitor, they place themselves behind it, and then all three, keeping step, begin a rapid march, uttering loud drumming and rhythmical notes in time with their movements, the notes of the birds behind coming in a rapid stream, while the leading bird utters loud single notes at regular intervals. The march ceases, the leader stretches out his wings, still emitting loud notes, while the other two, with puffed-out plumage, standing exactly abreast, stoop forward until the tips of their beaks touch the ground, and, sinking their voices to a murmur, remain for some time in this singular posture. The performance is then over; the birds all resume their natural attitudes, and the visitor takes his leave. It is quite certain that this display has no connection with the sexual feeling, for it is indulged in all the year round, at all hours of the day, and also during moonlight nights. It is simply the bird's manner of expressing its joyous spirits; for most living creatures—birds especially —have more or less well-defined methods of playing; and play-day with the Téru is every day, and at brief intervals. And yet the grave, pompous air of the birds, and the military precision of their movements, might easily lead an observer to attribute these displays to some more important motive. Play is not only indulged in with neighbours; there are many solitary Térus continually wandering about from place to place—probably young birds not yet settled in life—and when one of these vagrants passes near a pair he is immediately invited to join them, and when he alights all go through the performance together with great zest. In this case, however, as soon as it is over, the strange bird is attacked with great spirit and chased away; and if by chance he comes down again near them, they hasten to drive him up with increased fury. He is wanted only for five or six minutes and must not outstay his welcome.

While watching their antics, which the gauchos call the Téru's quadrilles, a curious subject of enquiry suggested itself to my mind. It appeared to me that its manner of playing has had a reflex effect strong enough to mark the bird's whole character—language, bearing, and habits being coloured by it, and even the domestic relations interfered with. And with regard to the latter point, though it is the rule that each cock bird has only one hen, I have known several instances of a cock with two hens, the two females laying their eggs in one nest and taking turns in sitting on them. I have also found instances of two males to one female; and in one case where I watched the birds I noticed that when the female was on the nest the males stood over her, one on each side.

I once had my attention drawn to a large concourse of Térus by the strange behaviour of two individuals amongst them, and I stayed to watch their proceedings. It was in the dry, hot weather, and a great many birds had congregated to drink at a lagoon. Some hundreds of them were standing about, quietly preening their feathers, and in the middle of the flock two birds were conspicuously marching about, stiff and upright as a couple of soldiers engaged in some military exercise, and uttering loud notes full of authority. Every few minutes a fresh bird would arrive and alight at some distance from the water, on which the two noisy birds would bustle up, and, ranging themselves behind it, run it with loud drumming notes to the margin; then, standing close together, they would wait till its thirst was quenched, after which they would run it away to some distance from the water, of which they seemed to have made themselves dispensers. For over an hour I continued watching them, and every bird that arrived was conducted to and from the water in this ceremonious manner.

Occasionally several couples unite and soar about in a compact flock; they divide into sets of three birds each, then hover for some time, all waving their wings exactly in time and screaming their notes in unison, and these movements seem like an imitation in the air of the usual marching and drumming performance on the ground.

The breeding-season of the Térus begins as early as the month of June in favourable seasons; severe cold, drought, or other causes sometimes delay it to August. The nest is a shallow circular hollow made by the bird on the level plain, and lined with broken grass-stems and small fragments of thistle-stalks; the eggs are four, rather sharply pointed at one end, and have an olive-green ground colour spotted with black. The eggs in different nests vary greatly in size, ground colour, and in the amount of black they are marked with, no two birds laying eggs exactly alike.

While the female is on the nest the male keeps watch at a distance of twenty or thirty yards, and utters a low warning cry in case of danger. The female leaves the nest sometimes by running, but oftener flies from it, and by marking the spot she rises from it is easy to find the nest on the open level pampas. In the course of a morning's ride I have picked up as many as sixty-four eggs. During incubation the birds are excessively watchful and jealous, their irritability increasing with the growth of the chick in the shell; and at that time they will attack any bird of prey approaching the nest with great fury. When approached by a human being they fly to meet him when he is still far from them, and hovering, with loud screams, over him, dash down at intervals, threatening to strike with their wing-spurs, coming very close to his head. Unable to intimidate the enemy with this show of violence the bird changes its tactics, and, alighting at some distance, counterfeits the action of a bird seeking its nest. With well-acted caution and secrecy in its manner, it runs silently along, stooping low, and having found a slight nest-like depression on the surface, sits on it, half opens its wings, and begins gathering all the small sticks or straws within its reach and carefully arranges them about it, as most ground-breeding birds do when incubating. Sometimes also, like many other species, it tries to lead one away from the nest by feigning lameness; but the former instinct of seeking and sitting on an imaginary nest, which I have not observed in any other bird, seems far more complex and admirable.

When sheep in a flock pass over the nest, the bird stands on it to defend its eggs; and then its loud cries and outspread wings often serve to bring the sheep, from motives of curiosity, about it. Even with a dozen sheep clustered round it the bird stands undaunted, beating their faces with its wings; but, unhappily for it, if the shepherd is following, the loud cries of the bird bring him to the spot, and the eggs so bravely defended are taken.

SLENDER-BILLED PLOVER

Oreophilus ruficollis (Wagl.)

SLENDER-BILLED PLOVER

Oreophilus ruficollis

Above grey, varied with yellowish brown and striped with black on the back and wing-coverts; front and superciliaries yellowish brown; stripe through the eye blackish; wings blackish with white shafts, their under surface white; tail grey, with a black subterminal bar on the lateral feathers; beneath grey; throat rusty reddish; below the breast a black band or patch; bill dark, feet red; length 10, wing 6.5 inches.

THIS pretty and singular Plover, with a bill like a Sandpiper, inhabits South Patagonia and the Falklands. In the autumn it migrates north, and during the cold season is found sparsely distributed throughout the Argentine States, and passes into Bolivia and Peru. On the pampas it is most abundant in April, but most of the birds seen during that month are travellers to warmer latitudes.

It is a shy and exceedingly active bird, somewhat larger than the Golden Plover in size, and in the Plata district is usually called *Chorlo canela*, from the prevailing cinnamon-red of the plumage. It is distinguished in the family it belongs to by the great length of its straight, slender, probe-like bill, unlike that of any other Plover; and it also has other structural peculiarities, the toes being exceptionally short and thick, the frontal bone curiously modified, and the eyes enormously large, like those of a nocturnal species. I do not think, however, that it migrates by night, as I have never heard its peculiar passage-cry after dark. A flock is usually composed of from a dozen to thirty individuals, and when on the ground they scatter widely, running more rapidly than any other Plover I am acquainted with. When they travel the flight is swift and high, the birds much scattered. They possess no mellow or ringing notes like other members of the Plover family ; on the ground they are silent, but when taking wing invariably utter a long, tremulous, reedy note, with a falling inflection, and usually repeated three or four times. The sound may be imitated by striking on the slackened stings of a guitar. This cry is frequently uttered while the birds are migrating.

On the Rio Negro in Patagonia I observed this Plover only in the winter season ; but Durnford found it nesting in the valley of the Sengel in Chupat in the month of December.

PARAGUAY SNIPE

Gallinago paraguaiæ

Above brown, striped and barred with black and pale fulvous;
wings dark cinereous edged with white; tail of sixteen rectrices, of
which the outer pair are pin-shaped; beneath white, breast marbled
with blackish and brown; length 10.5, wing 9.1 inches.

THIS familiar bird, called *Agachona* in the vernacular,
from its habit of crouching close to the ground to
escape observation when approached, is abundant in
the Plata district and resident, although its sudden
and total disappearance from all the open wet places
where it is common in the winter gives one the
impression that it is migratory. The bird, however,
only retires to breed in the extensive lonely marshes.
The nest is a slight depression on the moist ground
close to the water, and lined with a little withered
grass. The eggs are four, pear-shaped, and spotted
with black on an olive-coloured ground.

After the summer heats are over Snipes suddenly
appear again all over the country, and at this season
they are frequently met with on the high and dry
grounds among the withered grass and thistles. In
favourable wet seasons they sometimes collect in
large flocks, numbering not less than five or six
hundred birds, and a flock of this kind will occasionally remain in one spot for several months without
breaking up. They usually frequent an open spot of
level ground where the water just covers the roots
of the short grass; here the birds keep close together
while feeding and are visible from a long distance;
but they become extremely wary, all raising their
heads in a very un-Snipe-like manner at the slightest
alarm, and taking flight with the readiness of Wild

Ducks. These flocks are, however, not often met with. Usually the Snipe is a solitary bird, crouches close when approached, and springs up suddenly when almost trodden on, loudly uttering its sharp scraping alarm-cry; after rising to a considerable height, flying in a wild erratic manner, it returns suddenly to the earth, often dropping into the grass within twenty yards of the spot it rose from.

It is indeed curious to see how these habits, characteristic of the Snipes all over the world, are so completely laid aside when the birds associate in large flocks.

Early and late in the day many individuals are usually on the wing engaged in their aerial pastimes, the singular grinding or scythe-whetting sounds caused by their feathers in their violent descent from a great height being distinctly audible at a distance of nearly a mile. It is heard throughout the winter at all hours of the day in mild, damp weather, and on moonlight nights often until after midnight.

HUDSONIAN GODWIT

Limosa hæmastica

In summer: Above dark brownish black, mixed on the head with longitudinal streaks of whitish, on the neck with pale chestnut, and with many of the feathers of the back spotted or edged with pale chestnut; wings and tail blackish, the upper half of the inner webs of the primaries and secondaries, the basal part of the outer rectrices, and a broad band across the upper tail-coverts pure white; beneath, cheeks and throat whitish, becoming pale chestnut on the neck, longitudinally striped with blackish; rest of under surface deeper chestnut, transversely barred with blackish. *In winter:* Above uniform dull brownish; head, neck, and under surface dirty white or pale buff; length 14.3, wing 8.5 inches.

THE Hudsonian Godwit, Mr. Seebohm tells us, " breeds on the tundras of North America north of the forest-growth, from Alaska to Baffin's Bay, but is rare at the western extremity of its range." In winter it goes far south, like most of the other *Grallæ*.

Durnford found it " common from April to September about the lagoons and arroyos to the south of Buenos Ayres "; and states that in habits it much resembles the Bar-tailed Godwit of Europe (*Limosa lapponica*). He also met with it in Chupat, and obtained two specimens there on the 13th of November, 1876.

I have met with it in flocks during the summer of the Southern Hemisphere, and these birds, as well as those obtained by Durnford, were undoubtedly visitors from the north; but invariably small flocks of half a dozen to thirty birds begin to appear on the pampas in April, and remain there, as Durnford says, until September, when the northern migrants are nearly due. These individuals must therefore breed near the extremity, or beyond the extremity, of South America. It is very curious, to say the least of it, that the Arctic and Antarctic regions of

America should possess the same species, and that, at opposite seasons of the year, it should winter in the same district, so far from the breeding-place of one set of individuals, and so near to that of the other ! Captain Abbott observed the Hudsonian Godwit in the Falkland Islands in flocks in the month of May (see *Ibis*, 1861, p. 156). These could not have been Alaska birds, but were no doubt southern breeders on their way north, for that they could winter so far south seems incredible.

ARGENTINE BLACK-HEADED GULL

Larus maculipennis

Head and nape brownish-black (in breeding dress); tail and under-parts white; mantle pale grey; primaries black or dark grey, tipped with white, and with large elongated white patches on the outer portions of first to fifth, followed by a subapical *black bar* (in *L. glaucodes* the lower portion is *white*); underwing *pale grey*; bill, legs, and feet blood-red; length 17, wing 11.5 inches.

THIS common Black-headed Gull is found through-out the Argentine country, down to Chupat in Pata-gonia, and is exceedingly abundant on the pampas of Buenos Ayres, where it is simply called *Gaviota* (Gull). In the month of October they congregate in their breeding-places—extensive inland marshes, partially overgrown with rushes. The nests are formed of weeds and rushes, placed just above the water and near together, several hundreds being sometimes found within an area of less than one quarter of an acre. The eggs are four in number, large for the bird, obtusely pointed, of a pale clay-colour, thickly spotted at the big end and sparsely on the other parts with black.

Every morning at break of day the Gulls rise up from their nests and hover in a cloud over the marsh, producing so great a noise with their mingled cries that it can be heard distinctly at a distance of two miles. The eggs are considered a great delicacy, resembling those of the Plover in taste and appear-ance, and are consequently much sought after, so that when the locality near which a gullery is situated becomes inhabited the birds have no chance of rearing their young, as the boys in the neighbour-hood ride into the marsh every morning to gather the eggs. The Gulls are, however, very tenacious of their old breeding-places, and continue even after years of persecution to resort to them.

The young birds are of a pale grey colour, mottled with dull brown, and have a whining, querulous cry. The plumage becomes lighter, through the autumn and winter, but it is not until the ensuing summer, when the dark brown nuptial hood is assumed, that the young birds acquire the perfect plumage—soft grey-blue above, and the white bosom with its lovely pink blush.

As soon as the young are able to fly the breeding-place is forsaken, the whole concourse leaving in a body, or scattering in all directions over the surrounding country; and until the following summer their movements depend entirely on food and water. If the weather is dry the Gulls disappear altogether; and if grasshoppers become abundant the country people wish for rain to bring the Gulls. When it rains then the birds quickly appear, literally from the clouds, and often in such numbers as to free the earth from the plague of devastating insects. It is a fine and welcome sight to see a white cloud of birds settle on the afflicted district; and at such times their mode of proceeding is so regular that the flock well deserves the appellation of an army. They sweep down with a swift, graceful flight and settle on the earth with loud, joyful cries, but do not abandon the order of attack when the work of devouring has begun. The flock often presents a front of over a thousand feet, with a depth of sixty or seventy feet; all along this line of battle the excited cries of the birds produce a loud, continuous noise; all the birds are incessantly on the move, some skimming along the surface with expanded wings, others pursuing the fugitives through the air, while all the time the hindmost birds are flying over the flock to alight in the front ranks, so that the whole body is steadily advancing, devouring the grasshoppers as it proceeds. When they first arrive they seem ravenously hungry, and after gorging themselves they fly to the water, where after drinking they cast up their food and then go back to renew the battle.

In spring these Gulls come about the farms to follow the plough, filling the new-made furrows from end to end, hovering in a cloud over the ploughman's head and following at his heels, a screaming, fighting multitude. Wilson's expression in describing a northern species, that its cry " is like the excessive laugh of a negro," is also descriptive of the language of our bird. Its peculiar cry is lengthened at will and inflected a hundred ways, and interspersed with numerous short notes like excited exclamations. After feeding they always fly to the nearest water to drink and bathe their feathers, after which they retire to some open spot in the neighbourhood where there is a carpet of short grass. They invariably sit close together with their bills toward the wind, and the observer will watch the flock in vain to see one bird out of this beautiful order. They do not stand up to fly, but rise directly from a sitting posture. Usually the wings are flapped twice or thrice before the body is raised from the ground.

In some seasons in August and September, after a period of warm, wet weather, the larvæ of the large horned beetle rise to the surface, throwing up little mounds of earth as moles do ; often they are so numerous as to give the plains, where the grass has been very closely cropped, the appearance of being covered with mud. These insects afford a rich harvest to the Spur-winged Lapwing (*Vanellus cayennensis*), which in such seasons of plenty are to be seen all day diligently running about, probing and dislodging them from beneath the fresh hillocks. The Gulls, unprovided with a probing beak, avail themselves of their superior cunning and violence to rob the Lapwings; and I have often watched their proceedings for hours with the greatest interest. Hundreds of Lapwings are perhaps visible running busily about on all sides; near each one a Gull is quietly stationed, watching the movements of its intended dupe with the closest attention. The instant a great snow-white grub is extracted the Gull makes a rush to seize it, the Lapwing flies, and a violent chase ensues. After a hundred vain doublings the Plover drops the prize, and slopes toward the earth with a disappointed cry; the pursuer checks his flight, hovers a moment watching the grub fall, then drops down upon it, gobbles it up, and hastens after the Lapwing to resume his watch.

Many of these Gulls haunt the estancias to feed on the garbage usually found in abundance about cattle-breeding establishments. When a cow is slaughtered they collect in large numbers and quarrel with the domestic poultry over the offal. They are also faithful attendants at the shepherd's hut; and if a dead lamb remains in the fold when the flock goes to pasture they regale on it in company with the Chimango. The great *saladeros*, or slaughter-grounds, which were formerly close to Buenos Ayres, were also frequented by hosts of these neat and beautiful scavengers. Here numbers were seen hovering overhead, mingling their excited screams with the bellowing of half-wild cattle and the shouts of the slaughterers at their rough work; and at intervals, wherever a little space is allowed them, dropping down to the ground, which reeked with blood and offal, greedily snatching up whatever morsels they could seize on, yet getting no stain or speck on their delicate dress of lily-white and ethereal blue.

On the open pampas their curiosity and anger seem greatly excited at the appearance of a person on foot ; no sooner has the Gull spied him than it sweeps toward him with a rapid flight, uttering loud, indignant screams that never fail to attract all of its fellows within hearing distance. These all pass and repass, hovering over the pedestrian's head, screaming all the time as if highly incensed, and finally retire, joining their voices in a kind of chorus and waving their wings upwards in a slow, curious manner ; but often enough, when they are almost out of sight, they suddenly wheel about and hurry back screaming, with fresh zeal, to go through the whole pretty but annoying performance again.

GREAT GREBE

Æchmophorus major

Above blackish ; occipital crest divided, bronzy black ; wide bar across the wing white ; beneath white ; chin dark ashy ; neck, breast, and sides of belly (in adult) more or less red ; bill yellowish, feet dark ; length 21, wing 8 inches.

THIS Grebe is called in the vernacular *Macas cornudo*—the first word being the Indian generic name for the Grebes, while *cornudo* signifies horned, from the bird's habit of erecting, when excited, the feathers of the nape in the form of a horn. The species is found throughout Eastern Argentina, from its northern limits to Central Patagonia, where Durnford found it common and resident. On the Rio Negro I found it abundant, and it was formerly just as common along the Plata river, but owing to its large size and the great beauty of its lustrous under-plumage it is very much sought after and is becoming rare.

It is impossible to make this Grebe leave the water, and when discovered in a small pool it may be pursued until exhausted and caught with the hand ; yet it must occasionally perform long journeys on the wing when passing from one isolated lake to another. Probably its journeys are performed by night.

There is little diversity in the habits of Grebes, and only once have I seen one of these birds acting in a manner which seemed very unusual. This Grebe was swimming about and disported itself in a deep, narrow pool, and showed no alarm at my presence, though I sat on the margin within twenty-five yards of it. I saw it dive and come up with a small fish about three inches long in its beak ; after sitting motionless for a little while, it tossed the fish away to a considerable distance with a sudden jerk of its beak, and then at the instant the fish touched the water it dived again. Presently it emerged with the same fish, but only to fling it away and dive as before; and in this way it released and recaptured it about fifteen times, and then, tired of play, dropped it and let it escape.

Mr. Gibson has the following note on the breeding habits of the Great Grebe, as observed at Ajó, near the mouth of Rio de La Plata: "*P. major* breeds about the end of August, placing its nest in the thickest rushes of the swamp. The nest, built of wet water-weeds, is raised just above the level of the water; and I have twice seen the sitting bird hastily draw some weeds over the eggs before leaving them, on my approach. The clutch consists of three; and these are of the usual Grebe colour, generally much soiled and stained."

There are four more species of Grebe in Argentina: the Bright-cheeked Grebe, *Podiceps caliparæus*, confined to southern S. America; Rolland's Grebe, *Podiceps rollandi*, also confined to the south of the continent; the American Dabchick, *Tachybaptes dominicus*, inhabiting Central and S. America; and the Thick-billed Grebe, *Podilymbus podiceps*, found in both North and South America.

SPOTTED TINAMU

Nothura maculosa

Above pale yellowish brown, barred with black and brown and streaked with fulvous white; wing-feathers ashy black, crossed on both webs by fulvous bands; beneath rich yellowish brown; throat white; breast and flanks spotted and banded with brownish black; bill and feet yellowish brown; length 11, wing 5.5 inches. Female similar, but larger.

THE *Perdiz común* or Common Partridge of the pampas, as it is always called—the naturalist's name of Tinamu being utterly unknown in the southern part of South America—is much smaller than the *Perdiz grande,* but in its form, slender curved beak, bare legs, and in the yellowish mottled plumage, generally resembles it. It also inhabits the same kind of open grassy country, and is abundant everywhere on the pampas and as far south as the valley of the Rio Negro in Patagonia. It is solitary; but a number of individuals are usually found in proximity; and in lonely places on the pampas, where they are excessively abundant, I have seen three or four meet together and play in the manner of kittens, darting out from a place of concealment at each other, the pursued bird always escaping by turning off at right angles or by suddenly crouching down and allowing the pursuer to spring over it.

It is very tame in disposition, and flies so reluctantly that it is not necessary to shoot them where they are very abundant, as any number can be killed with a long whip or stick. It moves on the ground in a leisurely manner, uttering as it walks or runs a succession of low whistling notes. It has two distinct songs or calls, pleasing to the ear and heard all the year round; but with greater frequency in spring, and where the birds are scarce and much persecuted, in spring only. One is a succession of twenty or thirty short impressive whistling notes of great compass, followed by half a dozen rapidly uttered notes, beginning loud and sinking lower till they cease; the other call is a soft continuous trill, which appears to swell mysteriously on the air, for the listener cannot tell whence it proceeds; it lasts several seconds, and then seems to die away in the distance.

It is an exceedingly rare thing to see this bird rise except when compelled. I believe the power of flight is used chiefly, if not exclusively, as a means of escape from danger. The bird rises up when almost trodden upon, rushing through the air with a surprising noise and violence. It continues to rise at a decreasing angle for fifty or sixty yards, then gradually nears the earth, till, when it has got to a distance of two or three hundred yards, the violent action of the wing ceases and the bird glides along close to the earth for some distance, and either drops down or renews its flight. I suppose many birds fly in much the same way; only this Tinamu starts forward with such amazing energy that until this is expended and the moment of gliding comes, the flight is just as ungovernable to the bird as the motion of a brakeless engine, rushing along at full speed, would be to the driver. The bird knows the danger to which this peculiar character of its flight exposes it so well that it is careful to fly only to that side where it sees a clear course. It is sometimes, however, compelled to take wing suddenly, without considering the obstacles in its path; it also often miscalculates the height of an obstacle, so that for Tinamus to meet with accidents when flying is very common. In the course of a short ride

of two miles, during which several birds sprang up
before me, I have seen three of these Tinamus dash
themselves to death against a fence close to the path,
the height of which they had evidently misjudged. I
have also seen a bird fly blindly against the wall of
a house, killing itself instantly. A brother of mine
told me of a very curious thing he once witnessed.
He was galloping over the pampas, with a very
violent wind blowing in his face, when a Tinamu
started up before his horse. The bird flew up into
the air vertically, and, beating its wings violently,
and with a swiftness far exceeding that of its ordinary
flight, continued to ascend until it reached a vast
height, then came down again, whirling round and
round, striking the earth a very few yards from the
spot where it rose, and crushing itself to a pulp with
the tremendous force of the fall. It is very easy to
guess the cause of such an accident : while the
Tinamu struggled blindly to go forward, the violent
wind, catching the under surface of the wings, forced
it upwards, until the poor bird, becoming hopelessly
confused, fell back to earth. I have often seen a
Swallow, Gull, or Hawk, soaring about in a high
wind, suddenly turn the under surface of its wings
to the wind and instantly shoot straight up, apparently
without an effort, to a vast height, then recover itself,
and start off in a fresh direction. The Tinamu,
when once launched on the atmosphere, is at the
mercy of chance ; nevertheless had this incident
been related to me by a stranger I should not have
recorded it.

This Tinamu is frequently run down and caught
by well-mounted gaucho boys ; the bird frequently
escapes into a kennel in the earth, but when it sees
no refuge before it and is hotly pursued, it sometimes
drops dead. When caught in the hand they " feign

death," or swoon, but on being released quickly recover their faculties.

The nest is a slight hollow scratched in the ground under a thistle or in the grass, and lined with a few dry leaves. The number of eggs laid varies from five to eight. These are elliptical, with polished shells, and as a rule are of a wine-purple colour; but the hue varies somewhat, some eggs having a reddish tinge and others a deep liver-colour.

In Patagonia the Spotted Tinamu is replaced by the very closely allied Darwin's Tinamu, *Nothura darwini*.

This species, called *Perdiz chico*, or Little Partridge, by the natives, is somewhat smaller and paler in colouring than the common Tinamu of the pampas, but very closely resembles the young of that species. It inhabits Patagonia, and is nowhere very numerous, but appears to be thinly and equally distributed on the dry, sterile plains of that region, preferring places abounding in thin scrub. In disposition it is extremely shy, and when approached springs up at a distance ahead and runs away with the greatest speed and apparently much terrified. Sometimes when thus running it utters short whistled notes like the allied species. It rises more readily and with less noise than the pampas bird, and has a much higher flight. It has one call-note, heard only in the love-season— a succession of short whistling notes, like those of the *N. maculosa*, but without the rapidly uttered conclusion.

The nest is made under a small scrubby bush, and contains from five to seven eggs, in form and colour like those of *N. maculosa*, except that the reddish-purple tint is paler.

COMMON RHEA

Rhea americana

Above, head blackish; neck whitish, becoming black at the base
of the neck and between the shoulders; rest slatey grey; beneath,
throat and upper neck whitish, becoming black at the base of the neck,
whence arise two black lateral crescents, one on either side of the
upper breast; rest of under surface whitish; front of tarsus throughout covered with broad transverse scutes; length about 52 inches.

THE Common Rhea (called *Ñandú* in the Guarani
language, *Chueké* by the pampas Indians, and Ostrich
by Europeans) is found throughout the Argentine
Republic down to the Rio Negro in Patagonia, and,
in decreasing numbers, to a considerable distance
south of that river. Until within very recent times
it was very abundant on the pampas, and I can
remember the time when it was common within
forty miles of Buenos Ayres city. But it is now
becoming rare, and those who wish to have a hand
in its extermination must go to a distance of three
or four hundred miles from the Argentine capital
before they can get a sight of it.

The Rhea is peculiarly well adapted, in its size,
colour, faculties, and habits, to the conditions of
the level woodless country it inhabits; its lofty
stature, which exceeded that of any of its enemies
before the appearance of the European mounted
hunter, enables it to see far; its dim grey plumage,
the colour of the haze, made it almost invisible to
the eye at a distance, the long neck being so slender
and the bulky body so nearly on a level with the tall
grasses; while its speed exceeded that of all other
animals inhabiting the same country. When watching
the chase of Ostriches in the desert pampas, abounding in giant grasses, it struck me forcibly that this

manner of hunting the bird on horseback had brought
to light a weakness in the Rhea—a point in which
the correspondence between the animal and its environment is not perfect. The Rhea runs smoothly
on the surface, and where the tall grass-tussocks are
bound together, as is often the case, with slender
twining plants, its legs occasionally get entangled,
and the bird falls prostrate, and before it can struggle
up again the hunter is close at hand and able to
throw the *bolas*—the thong and balls, which, striking
the bird with great force, wind about its neck, wings,
and legs, and prevent its escape. When I questioned
Ostrich hunters as to this point they said that it was
true that the Rhea often falls when running hotly
pursued through long grass, and that the deer
(*Cervus campestris*) never falls because it leaps over
the large tussocks and all such obstructions. This
small infirmity of the Rhea would not, however,
have told very much against it if some moderation
had been observed in hunting it, or if the Argentine
Government had thought fit to protect it ; but in
La Plata, as in North America and South Africa, the
licence to kill, which every one possesses, has been
exercised with such zeal and fury that in a very few
more years the noblest Avian type of the great bird-
continent will be as unknown on the earth as the
Moa and the *Æpyornis*.

The Rhea lives in bands of from three or four to
twenty or thirty individuals. Where they are not
persecuted they show no fear of man, and come about
the houses, and are as familiar and tame as domestic
animals. Sometimes they become too familiar. At
one estancia I remember an old cock bird that constantly came alone to feed near the gate, which had
so great an animosity against the human figure in
petticoats that the women of the house could not go

out on foot or horseback without a man to defend
them from its attacks. When the young are taken
from the parent bird they become, as Azara truly
says, " domestic from the first day," and will follow
their owner about like a dog. It is this natural tame-
ness, together with the majesty and quaint grace of
its antique form, which makes the destruction of
the Rhea so painful to think of.

When persecuted, Rheas soon acquire a wary
habit, and escape by running almost before the
enemy has caught a sight of them; or else crouch
down to conceal themselves in the long grass; and
it then becomes difficult to find them, as they lie
close, and will not rise until almost trodden on. Their
speed and endurance are so great that, with a fair
start, it is almost impossible for the hunter to over-
take them, however well mounted. When the bird
is running, the wings hang down as if injured,
but usually one wing is raised and held up like a
great sail, for what reason it is impossible to say.
When hard pressed, the Rhea doubles frequently
and rapidly at right angles to its course; and if the
pursuer's horse is not well trained to follow the bird
in all its sudden turns without losing ground he is
quickly left far behind.

In the month of July the love-season begins, and
it is then that the curious ventriloquial bellowing,
booming, and wind-like sounds are emitted by the
male. The young males in the flock are attacked
and driven off by the old cock-bird; and when
there are two old males they fight for the hens. Their
battles are conducted in a rather curious manner,
the combatants twisting their long necks together
like a couple of serpents, and then viciously biting
at each other's heads with their beaks; meanwhile
they turn round and round in a circle, pounding

the earth with their feet, so that where the soil is wet or soft they make a circular trench where they tread. The females of a flock all lay together in a natural depression in the ground, with nothing to shelter it from sight, each hen laying a dozen or more eggs. It is common to find thirty to sixty eggs in a nest, but sometimes a larger number, and I have heard of a nest being found containing one hundred and twenty eggs. If the females are many the cock usually becomes broody before they finish laying, and he then drives them with great fury away and begins to incubate. The hens then drop their eggs about on the plains; and from the large number of wasted eggs found it seems probable that more are dropped out of than in the nest. The egg when fresh is of a fine golden yellow, but this colour grows paler from day to day, and finally fades to a parchment-white.

After hatching the young are assiduously tended and watched over by the cock, and it is then dangerous to approach the Rhea on horseback, as the bird with neck stretched out horizontally and outspread wings charges suddenly, making so huge and grotesque a figure that the tamest horse becomes ungovernable with terror.

Eagles and the large Carrion Hawk are the enemies the Rhea most fears when the young are still small, and at the sight of one flying overhead he crouches down and utters a loud snorting cry, whereupon the scattered young birds run in the greatest terror to shelter themselves under his wings.

Darwin's Rhea, *Rhea darwini*, differs little in colouring from the Common Rhea, which it replaces south of the Rio Negro. From this river it ranges south to the Straits of Magellan. The Indians call it " *Molú Chueké* "—short or dwarf Chueké; its

Spanish name is " *Avestruz petizo.*" They were formerly very abundant along the Rio Negro; unhappily some years ago their feathers commanded a very high price; Gauchos and Indians found that hunting the Ostrich was their most lucrative employment; consequently these noble birds were slaughtered in such numbers that they have been almost exterminated wherever the nature of the country admits of their being chased. When on the Rio Negro I was so anxious to obtain specimens of this Rhea that I engaged several Indians by the offer of a liberal reward to hunt for me, but they failed to capture a single adult bird. I can only set down here the most interesting facts I was able to collect concerning its habits, which are very imperfectly known.

When pursued it frequently attempts to elude the sight by suddenly squatting down amongst the bushes, which have a grey foliage to which the colour of its plumage closely assimilates. When hard pressed it possesses the same habit as the Common Rhea of raising the wings alternately and holding them up vertically: and also doubles suddenly like that species. Its speed is greater than that of the Common Rhea, but it is sooner exhausted. In running it carries its head stretched forward almost horizontally, which makes it seem lower in stature than the allied species—hence the vernacular name of " Short Ostrich." It is found in flocks of from three or four to thirty or more individuals. It begins to lay at the end of July, that is, a month before the *Rhea americana.* Several females lay in one nest, which is merely a slight depression lined with a little dry rubbish; as many as fifty eggs are sometimes found in one nest. A great many wasted or *huacho* eggs, as they are called, are also found at a distance from the nest.

I examined a number of eggs brought in by the hunters, and found them vary greatly in shape, size, and colour. The average size of the eggs was the same as those of the Common Rhea ; in shape they were more or less elliptical, scarcely any two being precisely alike. The shell has a fine polish, and when newly laid the colour is deep, rich green. They soon fade, however, and the side exposed to the sun first assumes a dull mottled green ; then this colour fades to yellowish, and again to pale stone-blue, becoming at last almost white. The comparative age of each egg in the nest may be known by the colour of the shell. The male incubates and rears the young ; and the procreant habits seem altogether like those of *Rhea americana*.

The young are hatched with the legs feathered to the toes ; these leg-feathers are not shed, but are gradually worn off, as the bird grows old, by continual friction against the stiff, scrubby vegetation. In adults usually a few scattered feathers remain, often worn down to mere stumps ; but the hunters told me that old birds are sometimes taken with the legs entirely feathered, and that these birds frequent plains where there is very little scrub. The plumage of the young is dusky grey, without white and black feathers. When a year old they acquire by moulting the mottled plumage of the adults, but do not attain their full size until the third year.

AFTERWORD

In the 1860s and 1870s, Hudson travelled widely in Brazil, Uruguay and Patagonia studying the natural history of the region and partially supporting himself collecting bird skins. These he carefully preserved and annotated, and sent to Spencer Baird, who was building an authoritative collection at the Smithsonian Institution. After Smithsonian money for further collections in the area dried up, Hudson was able to send skins to the Zoological Society of London. Soon his writings were being published in the Society's *Proceedings* and Hudson's career as a naturalist was launched. In 1888–89, *Argentine Ornithology*, which Hudson had authored with P.L. Sclater, was published in two volumes. Hudson's contributions to these volumes were later issued by themselves in the two-volume set of *Birds of La Plata* (1920). It is from these later books that this particular edition was formed.

The foundation of Hudson's work in *Argentine Ornithology* was his collection of field notes from the sixties and seventies. Intense, personal, and enthusiastic, his observations show the mind of a gifted naturalist at work in a largely unexplored field.

Bird taxonomy has undergone many revisions since 1888 and both the common and Latin names in *Argentine Ornithology* are often inaccurate according to today's system. The following list is an attempt to update the nomenclature; however, it may not be entirely accurate. Hudson's original descriptions have been carefully compared with those in *A Guide to the Birds of South America* by de Schawnses to determine, if possible, the 1970 counterparts of the original birds. These names were then updated with *Checklist of the World's Birds* and *A Complete Checklist of the Birds of the World*. More changes in taxonomy are bound to occur, but Hudson's beautifully evocative "bird biographies" will continue to speak to anyone who has every wondered at the mysteries of bird lore. — JUDITH YOUNG

1920 NOMENCLATURE	CONTEMPORARY NOMENCLATURE
1. Patagonian Mocking-bird *Mimus patagonicus*	1. Patagonian Mocking-bird *Mimus patagonicus*
2. White-banded Mocking-bird *Mimus triurus*	2. Same
3. House-Wren *Troglodytes furvus*	3. House-Wren *Troglodytes aedon*
4. Bank-martin *Atticora cyanoleuca*	4. Black-collared Swallow *Atticora melanoleuca*
5. Long-tailed Reed-finch *Donacospiza albifrons*	5. Same
6. Red-billed Ground-finch *Embernagra platensis*	6. Great Pampa-finch *Embernagra platensis*
7. Yellow House-Sparrow *Sycalis pelzelni*	7. Saffron-billed Sparrow *Arremon flavirostris*
8. Screaming Cow-bird *Molothrus rufoaxillaris*	8. Same
9. Red-breasted Marsh-bird *Leistes superciliaris*	9. White-browed Blackbird *Leistes superciliaris*
10. Military Starling *Trupialis defilippii*	10. Red-breasted Blackbird *Leistes militaris*
11. Black-crowned Tyrant *Taenioptera coronata*	11. Black-crowned Monjita *Xolmis coronata*
12. Bienteveo Tyrant *Pitangus bolivianus*	12. Great Kiskadee *Pitangus sulphuratus*
13. Oven-bird *Furnarius rufus*	13. Rufous Hornero *Furnarius rufus*
14. Rush-loving Spine-tail *Phleocryptes melanops*	14. Wren-like Rushbird *Phleocryptes melanops*
15. Hudson's Spine-tail *Synallaxis hudsoni*	15. Hudson's Canastero *Thripophaga hudsoni*
16. Firewood-gatherer *Anumbius acuticaudatus*	16. Firewood-gatherer *Anumbius annumbi*
17. Laughing Cachalote *Homorus gutturalis*	17. White-throated Cachalote *Pseudoseisura gutturalis*
18. Little Cock *Rhinocrypta lanceolata*	18. Grey Gallito *Rhinocrypta lanceolata*
19. Glittering Humming-bird *Chorostilbon splendidus*	19. Glittering-bellied Emerald *Chorostilbon areoventris*
20. Guira Cuckoo *Guira piririgua*	20. Guira Cuckoo *Guira guira*
21. Patagonian Parrot *Conurus patagonus*	21. Patagonian Conure *Cyanoliseus patagonus*
22. Green Parrakeet *Bolborhynchus monachus*	22. Sierra Parakeet *Bolborhynchus aymara*
23. Burrowing-Owl *Speotyto cunicularia*	23. Same
24. Crowned Eagle *Harpyhaliaeetus coronatus*	24. Crowned Solitary Eagle *Harpyhaliaetus coronatus*
25. Peregrine Falcon *Falco peregrinus*	25. Same
26. Pigmy Falcon *Spiziapteryx circumstinctus*	26. Spot-winged Falconet *Spiziapteryx circumcinctus*
27. Chimango, or Common Carrion Hawk *Milvago chimango*	27. Same
28. Carancho or Caracara *Polyborus tharus*	28. Common Caracara *Polyborus plancus*
29. Cocoi Heron *Ardea cocoi*	29. Same
30. Whistling Heron *Ardea sibilatrix*	30. Whistling Heron *Syrigma sibiliatrix*
31. Little Red Heron *Ardetta involucris*	31. Striated Heron *Butorides striatus*
32. Black-faced Ibis *Theristicus caudatus*	32. Buff-necked Ibis *Theristicus caudatus*
33. Crested Screamer *Chauna chavaria*	33. Northern Screamer *Chauna chavaria*
34. Black-necked Swan *Cygnus nigricollis*	34. Black-necked Swan *Cygnus melancoryphus*
35. Brazilian Teal *Querquedula brasiliensis*	35. Red-billed Whistling Duck *Dendrocygna autumnalis*
36. Brown Pintail *Dafila spinicauda*	36. Bronze-winged Duck *Anas specularis*
37. White-faced Pintail *Dafila bahamensis*	37. Bahama Pintail *Anas bahamensis*
38. Argentine Wood-Pigeon *Columba picazuro*	38. Picazuro Pigeon *Columba picazuro*
39. Spotted Dove *Zenaida maculata*	39. Spot-winged Pigeon *Columba maculosa*
40. Ypecaha Rail *Aramides ypecaha*	40. Giant Wood-rail *Aramides ypecaha*
41. Jacana *Parra jacana*	41. Wattled Jacana *Jacana jacana*
42. Spur-wing Lapwing *Vanellus cayennensis*	42. Southern Lapwing *Vanellus chilensis*
43. Slender-billed Plover *Oreophilus ruficollis*	43. Tawny-throated Dotterel *Oreopholus ruficollis*
44. Paraguay Snipe *Gallinago paraguatiae*	44. Common Snipe *Gallinago gallinago*
45. Hudsonian Godwit *Limosa haemastica*	45. Same
46. Argentine Black-headed Gull *Larus maculipennis*	46. Brown-hooded Gull *Larus maculipennis*
47. Great Grebe *Aechmophorus major*	47. Great Grebe *Podiceps major*
48. Spotted Tinamu *Nothura maculosa*	48. Spotted Nothura *Nothura maculosa*
49. Common Rhea *Rhea americana*	49. Greater Rhea *Rhea americana*

BIBLIOGRAPHY

de Schawnses, Rodolph Meyer. *A Guide to the Birds of South America.* Livingston Publishing Co., Wynnewood, PA. 1970.

Gruson, Edward S. *Checklist of the World's Birds.* Quadrange/New York Times Book Company, New York, NY. 1976.

Howard, Richard and Moore, Alick. *A Complete Checklist of the Birds of the World.* Oxford University Press, London. 1980.

Tomalin, Ruth. *W.H. Hudson, A Biography.* Faber & Faber, London. 1980.